W9-BVA-432

Connect to NCTM Standards 2000

Making the Standards Work at Grade 4

Francis (Skip) Fennell, Ph.D.
Honi J. Bamberger, Ph.D.
Thomas E. Rowan, Ph.D.
Kay B. Sammons
Anna R. Suarez

Creative Publications®
A Tribune Education Company

Acknowledgments

Project Editors → Diane Nieker, Jeff Stiegel

Writers → Tim Burnett, Marilyn Davis, Beth Sycamore

Writing and Editorial Services → MathLink, Inc.

Design Director → Karen Stack

Design → Gerta Sorensen-London

Project Coordinator → Barbara Quincer

Cover Illustration → Jim Dandy

Illustrators → Susan Aiello, Jim Dandy, Sarah Frederking

Production → Graphic Advantage, Ltd.

Manufacturing → Dallas Richards

© 2000 Creative Publications®, Inc.
Two Prudential Plaza
Chicago, IL 60601

Creative Publications is a registered trademark.
Printed in the United States of America.
All rights reserved.

This is an independent publication and is not affiliated with, or sponsored by, the NCTM. The NCTM 2000 Standards are not reproduced in this book. This book is designed to be read independently of the *Principles and Standards for School Mathematics* and to aid educators in preparing to teach in a manner consistent with the *Principles and Standards.*

Unless otherwise stated on selected pages in this book, no part of this publication may be reproduced, or copied into or stored in a retrieval system, or transmitted, in any form or by any means, electronic, mechanical, photocopying, recording, or otherwise, without prior written permission of the publisher.

ISBN 0-7622-1246-2
Catalog No. 21408
Customer Service 800-624-0822
http://www.creativepublications.com
1 2 3 4 5 6 7 8 MAL 05 04 03 02 01 00

Contents

Overview

Since *Curriculum and Evaluation Standards for School Mathematics* was released in 1989, much has been learned about how ideas work in the classroom and how students learn mathematics. The release of the *Principles and Standards for School Mathematics* creates an opportunity for us to examine our goals, our math curricula, and our teaching methods in light of these new insights and to consider practices and procedures that will improve school mathematics education. As did the original draft, *Principles and Standards* promotes ways for all educators to strengthen the teaching and learning of mathematics by addressing two important concerns: the characteristics of instructional programs that will provide high-quality mathematical experiences for students as they progress through school, and the mathematical content and processes students should know and use as they advance from grade to grade.

Content Standards

- Number and Operation
- Algebra
- Geometry
- Measurement
- Data Analysis and Probability

Process Standards

- Problem Solving
- Reasoning and Proof
- Communication
- Connections
- Representation

General Overview

Connect to NCTM Standards 2000 is designed to help you understand and implement the NCTM standards. Regardless of your teaching style, the information presented in this book will help you to make the standards work. *Principles and Standards* identifies ten standards. Five of those standards are described as content standards that organize all of mathematics into five broad areas of learning; they address *what* students learn. The other five standards, the process standards, are concerned with *how* students learn and how information is presented.

Today, more than ever, there is a need for all students to have a strong base in mathematics. This means that students do not just memorize facts and procedures, but that they have an understanding of mathematics and mathematical thinking. The interplay between content and process is complicated, but integrating the two is critical if our students are to receive the mathematics education they will need to function effectively in the world they will grow into.

The lessons contained within *Connect to NCTM Standards 2000* are organized into sections by content. Each section contains four lessons dealing with some aspect of that content standard. Each lesson demonstrates ways to develop the content by using the process standards. An overview highlights grade-level content skills and gives a brief description of the four lessons for that standard.

The last section of the book, entitled Create Your Own Lesson, is designed to help you develop lessons of your own that will comfortably incorporate the NCTM standards with your teaching style.

About the Lessons

Each content standard section contains four lessons that address some aspect of the content at the grade level. Three of the lessons have been specially developed to model ways the process standards can be used to develop the content being presented. The fourth lesson examines a hypothetical math textbook lesson in terms of how the process standards are incorporated into that lesson. Suggestions are offered for increasing the focus on three of the five process standards to create a more effective lesson. Then, a lesson is presented modeling how those suggestions can be implemented.

As you read through the lessons, keep in mind that what is offered is only one possible approach. You might have a completely different idea about how to develop the concept, and that's fine. These lessons are intended to provide examples of how the process standards can work to make mathematics lessons more meaningful, and to model questions and techniques that you might incorporate into your teaching. As you read through the lessons, pay attention to how the process standards are being used. Use the ideas presented as a springboard for your own ideas.

Each lesson is intended for a single class period. Some introduce a concept, others require that students have some experience with the concept, and still others are meant to be used at the end of a unit. As you examine these lessons, think about how and where they fit into your curriculum. Any of the lessons here can be used as a replacement for the comparable lesson in your current math program. Try the lessons and see the difference incorporating the process standards can make.

Creating Your Own Lessons

The last section of the book is designed to help you develop lessons of your own that incorporate the NCTM standards and are compatible with your teaching style. You will find questions to help you focus on ideas to consider as you begin to organize a standards-based lesson. You will also have an opportunity to follow the thoughts and decisions one person used in the process of developing a lesson.

About the Authors

Francis (Skip) Fennell, Ph.D.

Dr. Fennell was a member of the writing team of *Principles and Standards for School Mathematics* (NCTM, 2000). He has authored mathematics textbooks, materials for both students and teachers, and numerous articles for leading mathematics journals. Dr. Fennell has served on the Board of Directors of NCTM and as Program Officer of instructional materials and teacher enhancement within the Division of Elementary, Secondary, and Informal Education at the National Science Foundation. He has been selected as Outstanding Mathematics Educator by the Maryland Council of Teachers of Mathematics, and as Professor of the Year by both the Carnegie Foundation and Western Maryland College, where he is a professor of education.

Honi J. Bamberger, Ph.D.

Dr. Bamberger is a recognized math scholar and teacher. She has taught at both the elementary school and college levels, served as an associate research scientist and mathematics consultant for Johns Hopkins University, and contributed as a consultant and content writer for the "Numbers Alive" public television series. Dr. Bamberger has presented her research findings at mathematics conferences across the country, and has been an author for a number of mathematics textbooks. Currently, Dr. Bamberger is executive director of Insight, a consulting firm specializing in professional development in mathematics education.

Thomas E. Rowan, Ph.D.

Dr. Rowan was a member of the working group that wrote the K–4 section of the *Curriculum and Evaluation Standards for School Mathematics.* Since the Standards were first published, he has worked with many school systems to help bring about the transition to standards-based classroom mathematics instruction in grades K–8. Dr. Rowan is a frequent presenter at NCTM and author of mathematics texts and numerous articles on teaching and learning mathematics. He currently teaches at the University of Maryland where he focuses on methods of teaching elementary school mathematics.

Kay B. Sammons

Kay Sammons is currently Elementary Mathematics Supervisor for the Howard County Public Schools in Ellicott City, Maryland, where she is responsible for curriculum and staff development for elementary teachers. She is a frequent presenter at state and national mathematics conferences. In addition to serving as a reviewer for NCTM publications, she has written textbooks and teacher resource materials. Ms. Sammons was honored as Elementary Mathematics Teacher of the Year by the Maryland Council Teachers of Mathematics and as Outstanding Educator of the Year by that same organization.

Anna R. Suarez

Anna Suarez is a national consultant and program director for K–8 Mathematics at the National Science Foundation in Arlington, Virginia. Her participation in an NSF-funded research study, Cognitively Guided Instruction (C.G.I.), helped to develop teachers' knowledge of students' mathematical thinking as the basis for making instructional decisions. She has written staff development materials for both the *Investigations* curriculum and Insight.

About the Standards

The *Principles and Standards for School Mathematics 2000* are built around ten curriculum standards. Five of those standards address the mathematical content, or body of mathematical knowledge, that students should learn. Content standards prescribe *what* is to be taught in mathematics. The content standards are Number and Operation, Algebra, Geometry, Measurement, and Data Analysis and Probability.

The other five standards are process standards. The process standards describe *how* the content is delivered. They address how students will acquire the necessary mathematical content and how that knowledge will be applied. The five process standards are identified as Problem Solving, Reasoning and Proof, Communication, Connections, and Representation.

It should be pointed out that the content standards and process standards are not separate subsets of the whole, but are intricately interrelated. How mathematics is learned is as important as what mathematics is learned. The process standards help to "frame" how the content standards are presented.

It is possible to weave the process standards into the teaching of mathematics through a variety of methods. Students can and should be presented with meaningful problems to solve and situations that require them to reason through information to find solutions. They should be asked to defend their solutions and explain their thinking. In presenting a problem to students, connections might be made to a similar problem to build on previous learning. A representative model might be used to enhance students' understanding of a concept. Continuous communication, written and oral, will provide feedback about students' understanding.

For students to become mathematically powerful, it is essential that they be able to use process skills flexibly. They need to practice applying reasoning to solve problems and proving that their solutions are correct. They need to experiment with a variety of representations and have the ability to use them in solving problems and in illustrating their thinking. They should be able to communicate their mathematical thinking and solutions to the teacher and to other students both orally and in writing. Making connections between problems within mathematics is as essential as is making mathematical connections to disciplines outside of mathematics. The importance of how these processes interrelate and work together cannot be overemphasized.

Content Standards

Number and Operation

Algebra

Geometry

Measurement

Data Analysis and Probability

Process Standards

Problem Solving

Reasoning and Proof

Communication

Connections

Representation

Intermediate Problem Solving

PROBLEM SOLVING IS AT THE HEART of mathematics—it is what mathematicians do. Balance is achieved through the interrelationship of conceptual learning, basic skills, and problem solving. Students need to develop concepts with concrete representations to ensure understanding and to build a strong foundation. They need basic skills in order to apply their understandings with efficiency. But most importantly, they need good problems to solve, problems in which they can apply their conceptual understandings and utilize basic skills.

In its simplest form, problem solving means finding a solution when the answer is not readily apparent. Because problem solving does not always follow a uniform plan, students need to develop persistence to be able to work problems through to the end. Sometimes persistence means changing direction. *Well, we know that way doesn't work. What should we try next? Is there another way we can look at this problem?* Questions that encourage students to look for other options should be an integral part of the discussions that take place in mathematics classes.

Choosing problems that have relevance to students is an important factor in creating enthusiasm for problem solving. Often, the enthusiasm of the teacher translates into a positive disposition toward problem solving to students. If statements like, "Now that's an unusual problem. I wonder how we can find the answer," are part of a teacher's repertoire, children get the notion that problem solving is interesting and they are encouraged to use their own resources to find a path to the solution.

Acquiring a variety of strategies to access for problem solving is essential to experiencing success. Having flexibility to solve problems in different ways enables students to get "unstuck" if they reach a "dead end." It allows them to have other approaches to try. Students should be provided with instruction and practice in using a wide range of strategies to draw upon.

When intermediate grade students are presented with a problem which doesn't exactly conform to what has been learned previously, they need to develop strategies based on their skills and concepts.

A fourth grade teacher presented the following problem to the class:

> ***How many different rectangles can you find on your geoboard?***
>
> **Work with a partner and record your solutions on geoboard dot paper.**

Interesting communication ensued between students and teacher from the beginning of the lesson. *What is a rectangle?*

Scott responded, "A shape with four corners."

What is the word that mathematicians use to describe corners?

"They're angles," suggested Kiesha.

What do we know about the angles of a rectangle?

"They are all right angles," Armando stated.

Does anyone know how many degrees are in a right angle?

"Ninety degrees," contributed Ryan.

Show me a rectangle on your geoboard.

The students used their rubber bands to make rectangles on their geoboards. The teacher held up Kristen's geoboard. *What do you think about the shape Kristen found?*

"That's a square, not a rectangle," offered Anna.

"But a square is a rectangle," argued Kristen.

Following a discussion about the properties of rectangles and squares, the students were paired to begin their exploration. The teacher described the parameters of the problem. *Your task today is to find all the different rectangles you can on your geoboard. The rectangles must all be different. If the rectangle is just in a different place or flipped on its side, it doesn't count as being different.*

As the students were discovering and recording their "finds," the teacher checked to make sure there were no duplicates and prompted students to think of ways to create rectangles. *I wonder if you could find a rectangle that is tilted. Would that be different than the straight ones? Can you find a rectangle that is similar to this one, but a little larger?*

After students had found several rectangles, a class discussion was held for students to share their findings. Using an overhead model of a geoboard, different students demonstrated rectangles they had found. As each rectangle was identified, pairs tried to find the same one on their geoboard dot paper. If they were unable to find it, they were directed to construct it on their geoboard and record it on their geoboard dot paper. By the end of the math period, the class had found 15 different rectangles. The teacher let them know that they had done a wonderful job and then closed the lesson with a challenge. *There are 16 possible rectangles. Do you think someone will be able to find the 16th rectangle?*

This engaging problem-solving activity provides an example of how the processes work together in a lesson. Connections were made as students clarified definitions and represented shapes with geoboards and drawings. Communication was woven into all parts of the lesson from the introductory dialogue with the class through the questions posed to students during the exploration to the culminating discussion. Reasoning and proof was involved in identifying and proving that rectangles were different from one another.

Problem solving should be at the core of any mathematics curriculum. Through working well-chosen problems, students are challenged to apply the skills they have learned in new ways that expand their thinking and understanding of concepts. Students who are consistently presented with challenging problems learn to develop and apply new strategies. When they are also given opportunities to communicate their strategies with others and reflect on their thinking, their problem solving abilities are further enhanced.

Intermediate Reasoning and Proof

REASONING IS FUNDAMENTAL TO THE STUDY of mathematics—it is a state of mind that causes students to explore, to justify, and to validate. It permeates all content areas and all grade levels. Students are reasoning when they interpret data, when they solve problems, and when they view geometric patterns and shapes. As they are presented with new problems, they use reasoning skills to apply previously acquired information and to test the validity of their solutions. Reasoning is the process by which students make sense of mathematics.

As they develop mathematically, students learn that mathematics is a discipline based on an inherent set of rules. Reasoning begins with intuition. This intuition is used by the even the youngest children in their efforts to make sense of mathematics, and it should be encouraged as the basis of reasoning at all grade levels. This informal intuition will become the basis for reasoning through representations that are more formal and for proofs based upon the rules.

What are some ways reasoning and proof can be incorporated into the mathematics class? An excellent way is to ask questions that hold students accountable for their thinking. *How did you get your answer? Tell me how you thought about that. Why does your solution work? Do you think that strategy will always work?*

Piaget believed that for children to develop reasoning, it was imperative to have social interaction. A powerful means of achieving this interaction is through mathematical discussions. Designating time during the class for students to put forth their ideas for examination is critical. Students must

© Creative Publications

learn to explain and defend their thinking. They must also learn to detect unsound reasoning in explanations presented by other students. In any given class there will be a wide range of reasoning abilities. It is helpful for students with less mature reasoning to hear from those with well-developed skills. These mathematical discussions increase a student's repertoire of reasoning skills.

What do these mathematical discussions look like? A teacher typically presents a problem to the class that may be related to concepts being studied. Early in the year, before the multiplication algorithm was introduced, the following problem was presented to a fourth grade class.

What is 24 x 6?

After time was allowed for students to solve the problem, they were asked to share their responses.

- The first student reported that the answer was 144.
  When asked by the teacher to explain how he got the answer he said, "I multiplied 20 times 6 and got 120. Then I multiplied 4 × 6 and got 24. I added 120 and 24 and got 144."

- Another student responded, "I got 144 too, but I did it differently." When asked to explain how she got the answer, she responded, "I thought that 24 is close to 25 and 25 is like a quarter. So I thought of 6 quarters and that would be $1.50. But that is too much because there are only 24 and not 25 so I had to subtract 6 from $1.50. I got 144."

- A third student interjected, "I got 144 too, but I did it a different way. I broke 24 into 10 + 10 + 4 because it's easier for me to multiply tens. I multiplied 10 × 6 and got 60. I had to do it twice. I got 120. Then I multiplied the 6 times the 4 and got 24. I added it to the 120 and got 144."

The teacher asked if this third solution was related in any way to the others. One student said, "It's a lot like the first one, but instead of multiplying 20 × 6, 10 was multiplied by 6 and then doubled." Whether a student is explaining his answer to the class or listening to the explanation of another, the time spent on this kind of discussion is invaluable. All students benefit when they are asked to defend their answers as well as to reflect on someone else's solution to determine whether it makes sense.

© Creative Publications

Intermediate Communication

WHETHER BETWEEN TEACHER AND STUDENT, between a pair of students, or among groups of students, the communication skills of reading, writing, listening, and speaking provide the means for sharing ideas and promoting mathematical understanding. As students express their ideas through oral and written language, they have an opportunity to clarify their thinking and reinforce their own comprehension of the concepts they are working with. By listening to explanations given by their classmates, students are exposed to ideas they may not have thought of. This provides a greater network of connections among ideas and, in turn, enhances learning.

Ample opportunities to discuss mathematical ideas should be provided. One way to promote this is to present an interesting problem to the class, allow time to solve the problem, and then ask students to explain how they solved the problem. Providing a forum for a number of different solutions to be presented and defended by students results in rich dialogue. There is a very high level of mental activity associated with social interactions of this nature. Students who are afforded opportunities to take part in these mathematical conversations on a regular basis learn more effectively how to reason and defend their answers. In the process, they also learn to communicate and to clarify and refine their ideas, which leads to deeper understanding.

When students are able to communicate their ideas, the teacher is provided with insight into their thinking. As an example, the following problem might be given to students.

> **A minivan can seat 6 students plus the driver.** ***How many minivans will be needed to transport a class of 32 students on a field trip?***

Students will solve this problem in a variety of ways.

- They might draw rectangles to represent buses and put 6 tally marks in each rectangle to stand for the number of students each van will hold.
- Some might count by sixes.
- Students might apply the division algorithm to this problem—getting an answer of 5 remainder 2.

© Creative Publications

This last solution prompts an interesting discussion. *What does a remainder of 2 really mean in this problem? Can you have 2 students left over? Does a remainder make sense in this situation?* Going back to the question of how many minivans will be needed all together helps clarify the answer. Because the students have had additional time to review and reflect on the problem, their understanding is enhanced.

Putting ideas on paper is another means of helping students organize their thinking. Writing causes a student to reflect on ideas and refine them before committing that thinking to paper. Often, at the end of a lesson, students will be asked to communicate what they learned in the problem or investigation they just completed. This reflection can be an important tool for teachers in assessing their students' understanding. Words, pictures, numbers and symbols are all important parts of written communication that students have at their disposal, and students are becoming much more adept at using mathematical symbols to communicate their thinking. Many teachers use journal writing as a way for students to relate what they know about mathematics.

Intermediate students should be provided with regular opportunities to use both oral and written language and to share mathematical ideas with their teachers and peers on a daily basis.

Intermediate Connections

MAKING CONNECTIONS IN MATHEMATICS is a three-fold process. First, connections are made when one mathematical idea is used to build another. Second, connections are made among different mathematical ideas. Third, connections are made between mathematics and contexts outside the field of mathematics.

Because mathematics is an integrated discipline, treating it as a whole body of knowledge and focusing on the connections that occur naturally adds dimension to ideas and concepts. How is counting related to addition, addition to subtraction, addition to multiplication, multiplication to area? A cohesive curriculum that is clearly articulated from pre-kindergarten through the twelfth grade, one that connects the mathematical ideas within each grade as well as the mathematics between grade levels, is critical if those connections are to take place.

© Creative Publications

Making connections to prior mathematical experiences is vital for the understanding of how mathematical ideas build on one another. Teachers need to know what mathematics students learned previously in order to build on that knowledge. In a given unit of study, attention should be paid to ensure that mathematics concepts build upon one another from day to day in a coherent manner. Teachers should also be aware of what their students will be studying in subsequent grades so they can lay the foundation for obvious connections to further studies.

Mathematics permeates other subject areas as well as the physical world of students. The use of shapes and patterns is prevalent in art and architecture; measurement skills and classification skills are important in science; measurement skills and knowledge of fractions are utilized in cooking and building models; and measurement skills and data gathering and statistics are applied in the social sciences.

In grades 3–5, students will be building on the foundation laid in the primary grades. They will be taking their knowledge of addition and subtraction and connecting it to the study of multiplication and division. They will connect

division to the study of fractions. They will take what they have learned about identifying, building, and extending patterns to making predictions about patterns. Measurement in primary grades focused on nonstandard measures. Students will transfer that knowledge to working with standard measures. They will increase the sophistication of the study of data, probability, and statistics. Many of the concrete representations used in the primary grades will evolve to symbolic forms.

There are countless ways to make connections with the mathematics studied in these grades. For example, students enjoy taking surveys of their peers' preferences in food, music, movies, and games. This can be connected to collecting, organizing, and displaying the data in a way that makes sense—important skills that help students to better understand and interpret information presented in the world around them. Analyzing the data gathered from these surveys can be connected to interesting statistical problems. The teacher might pose the questions or have students generate their own.

Calculating the cost of having a class party that includes refreshments, prizes for games, and paper products is a relevant problem for intermediate age students. An activity of this type makes connections to a real world problem. Working in teams, students can estimate how much to order as they generate a menu and supplies that will be needed, and they can calculate costs to work within a given budget. This kind of problem also encourages them to do cost comparisons among various brands.

It is important for teachers to be conscious of connections that can be made in mathematics and to weave those connections into daily practice. When students are able to connect mathematical ideas both inside and outside of the classroom, they begin to see mathematics as a cohesive body of knowledge.

© Creative Publications

Intermediate Representation

REPRESENTATIONS PROVIDE VEHICLES for expressing and internalizing mathematical thought. They are a critical component in shaping the way students access, understand, express, and utilize mathematical ideas. Representations include physical objects, pictures, and symbols. They also include mental images, words, and ideas.

Representations can be formal or informal. Examples of formal representations are the conventional symbols, graphs, and diagrams traditionally introduced in school mathematics. Informal representations are often invented by students as a way of making sense of mathematical ideas and communicating those ideas to classmates or the teacher. Students should be allowed to create their own understanding and explanations to express relationships before more conventional representations are introduced. Connecting to their invented forms will facilitate a meaningful transition to thinking and communicating in the language of mathematics.

As teachers design lessons, choosing the representations they feel will best help students understand a concept becomes an important consideration. What shared mathematical language is needed to effectively communicate ideas? What manipulatives or models will be appropriate? How will students record their understanding of the concept? When is it appropriate to move from physical to symbolic representations?

In the intermediate grades students begin learning about multiplication conceptually, with concrete objects, often in groups or sets.

> ***If there are 3 sets of marbles and there are 3 marbles in each set, how many marbles are there all together?***

Students will use the marbles from the marble jar to make three groups and count the groups to discover there are 9. Students also learn they can represent that concept by drawing pictures of 3 marbles in three different groups. They extend that knowledge to represent the concept as repeated addition, writing $3 + 3 + 3 = 9$. In grades 3–5 students learn to represent the same situation as multiplication and write $3 \times 3 = 9$. This abstract equation makes sense to them because they have seen the connections through various representative models.

Intermediate grade students still continue to use non-conventional methods to help them interpret new concepts. For example, the teacher may pose the following problem.

Which is more, $\frac{1}{4}$ of a set of 16 items or $\frac{1}{3}$ of a set of 15 items?

Most students at this level do not yet have the means to approach this problem symbolically. Some students will use physical models, such as centimeter cubes to help them determine the answer. Many will make a drawing and will use various representations.

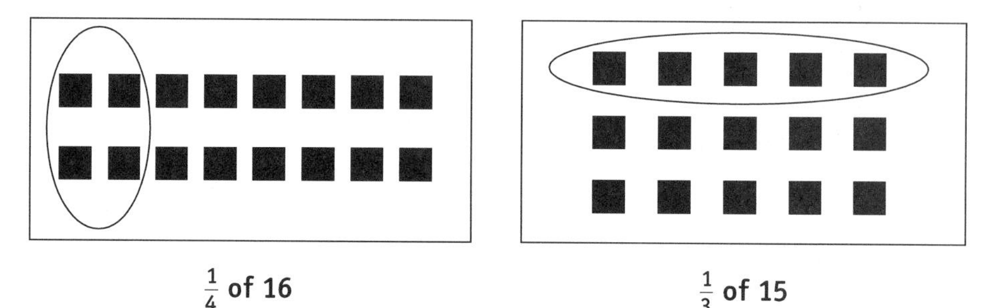

$\frac{1}{4}$ of 16 **$\frac{1}{3}$ of 15**

Students will be able to conclude that $\frac{1}{3}$ of 15 is a greater amount than $\frac{1}{4}$ of 16. This form of representation allows students to understand a process. It also provides an opportunity for the teacher to connect the visual representation with the equations $\frac{1}{3} \times 15 = 5$ and $\frac{1}{4} \times 16 = 4$ as another way of describing the results.

There are multiple representations for any mathematics concept. The greater the number of ways to represent the same idea, the greater the flexibility available in solving problems. For example, the number 25 can be thought of as 2 tens and 5 ones; as a quarter; as halfway between 1 and 50; as the square of 5; as an odd number; as one more than 24; as five less than 30; as 12 + 13; and so on. A student with access to this variety of representations of 25 is able to choose which version is useful for a particular situation.

One successful way to build multiple representations is to designate a number of the week and encourage students to build a repertoire of ways to represent that number. You might begin with a number such as 27, and ask students to find as many ways as they can to represent that number in 3 minutes. Record their findings on chart paper and post them for students to reflect upon. Revisit the problem for approximately 3 minutes each day. Encourage creative thinking by asking probing questions. *Is there a way to make 27 using multiplication AND division? Can 27 be made using three operations?* By the end of the week, you will have a chart full of interesting representations. If students engage in this type of activity on a regular basis, they will become fluid in their thinking about numbers.

$20 + 7 = 27$	$9 + 18 = 27$	$(4 \times 6) + 3 = 27$
$12 + 15 = 27$	$3 \times 9 = 27$	$30 - 3 = 27$
$(5 \times 5) + 2 = 27$		$(28 \div 4) + (2 \times 10) = 27$

Conclusion

The process standards are not an end, in and of themselves. Rather, they provide the advanced organizers or plan for lessons that present important mathematics content. Seeing connections among mathematical topics enables students to reason and make sense of new ideas and problem-solving situations they encounter. Through the process of communication, students are able to represent these new ideas either formally or informally.

Just as the process standards are interrelated, so are the process and content standards. For true mathematical thinking and learning to occur, both process and content need to be skillfully woven into and through each lesson. That is the goal to work toward.

Standard 1 **Number and Operation**

AT THE FOURTH GRADE LEVEL, number and operation include work with all four of the basic operations, developing estimation sense, and understanding the magnitude of larger numbers. Our lessons are derived from these important topics. They include a lesson on conceptualizing 1,000, a lesson that develops estimation skills, a lesson that emphasizes subtracting larger numbers with zeros in the minuend, and a lesson on interpreting remainders in division.

Three lessons model how the process standards can be used to teach content. A fourth lesson is a hypothetical textbook lesson that we have revised to be more standards based. These four lessons do not represent the entire curriculum, but rather provide glimpses of how, with a more concentrated effort to incorporate the process standards, better mathematics teaching and learning can be achieved.

One lesson we have chosen develops students' sense of 1,000. Through different representations, both physical and symbolic, students form a mental image of the quantity 1,000. Students also develop this image by communicating their thoughts and incorporating the thoughts of others into their thinking.

Another lesson we have chosen focuses students on the usefulness of developing estimation techniques. Through problem-solving situations, students realize that exact answers are not always required; that estimates of a sum can be found more quickly and can provide useful information. Students communicate about different ways to estimate and discuss how these estimates can be used to resolve the problem-solving situations.

A third lesson we have chosen focuses on interpreting remainders in division. Through problem solving, students will examine the same division problem in four contexts, each necessitating a different way to interpret the remainder. Students make visual representations of the problem situations to help them understand the differences, and use reasoning and proof to explain their conclusions.

The hypothetical textbook lesson we have chosen to revise is one that focuses on subtracting four-digit numbers with two or more consecutive zeros in the minuend. Students make connections and use reasoning to apply and extend what they already know about subtraction with one zero in the minuend. Students find that representing their work accurately decreases their chances of making an error.

Standard 1 Lessons

Recognizing 1,000

Using Estimation

Interpreting Remainders in Division

Subtracting Across Zeros

Recognizing 1,000

Introduction

Objective → Students will gain an understanding of 1,000 as a quantity and as a number by exploring its role in our place value system. They will use this knowledge of 1,000 to estimate solutions to computation problems.

Context → Students have an understanding of the place value of three-digit numbers and have solved and estimated sums and differences with three-digit numbers. They will go on to use their knowledge of 1,000 in our number system by applying it to operations with larger numbers.

NCTM Standards Focus

Students are developing a sense of the magnitude of 1,000. They use reasoning as they show how numbers grow from ones to hundreds to thousands in our number system. They generalize about the relationships between place values and prove their hypothesis as they represent and formulate different base-ten combinations that make 1,000. By exploring the concept of place value on their own with concrete materials, students formulate rules about how a digit changes value from one place to the next. In many programs, students mostly manipulate digits only and are asked to accept given rules.

Representation Students use physical objects in the classroom to represent the quantity of 1,000. They form mental pictures of the relative magnitude of a thousand as they think about groups of familiar objects that might represent the quantity 1,000. They use symbolic representations of the number as they analyze its place on a place value chart and the relationships between the places on the chart.

Communication Students discuss and learn from each other's strategies as they evaluate the magnitude of 1,000. Students communicate within small groups to come up with examples of familiar objects that exemplify the quantity 1,000.

Reasoning and Proof Students make predictions about the relationship between the place value positions in our number system. They test their predictions by showing 1,000 symbolically using combinations of numbers with different place values and by proving why these combinations of numbers make 1,000.

Teaching Plan

Materials → Student pages 22–23; base ten blocks; overhead projector

ASK STUDENTS TO GIVE EXAMPLES of things around the class room or school of which there are probably more or less than 100. For example, there are less than 100 students in the class, more than 100 students in the school. Introduce the concept of 1,000. How much is 1,000? Have students think about things in the classroom or the school of which they think there are 1,000 or more. As students list possible examples of things that represent the quantity 1,000, ask them what the quantity 1,000 represents. If students do not come up with it on their own, introduce them to the concept that 1,000 is equal to 10 times 100, or ten hundreds. Use base ten blocks to represent this equivalence.

Have students work in pairs or small groups to come up with a list of six examples of things around the classroom or school that represent the quantity 1,000 or more than 1,000. Tell students to be prepared to give examples from their list in class discussion and to explain the reasoning behind their choices. Students may come up with examples such as the following.

- 2 reams or packages of writing paper have 1,000 sheets of paper. One ream has 500 sheets and 500 + 500 = 1,000.
- 2 stacked math books might have more than 1,000 pages in all. One book may have more than 500 pages, and 2 × more than 500 pages = more than 1,000 pages.
- Depending on the size of the school, there might be more than 1,000 students in the school. (Students should explain by multiplying the average number of students per grade × the number of grades.)
- Through estimation and reasoning, there are more than 1,000 books in the school library.
- There are more than 1,000 cubes among sets of base ten blocks. Ten flats (100 cubes) equal 1,000 cubes.
- There are between 48 and 164 crayons in a box. There are between 20 and 25 students in the class. Each has a box of crayons. Therefore, there are at least 1,000 crayons in the classroom.
- There are more than 1,000 feet of hallways and classroom space in the school. (Students may estimate by measuring the size of their own classroom.)

f.y.i.

If some students find it difficult to grasp the magnitude of 1,000, get them started by suggesting some ideas for them to think about or investigate. *How many gallon jugs would it take to carry 1,000 marbles? How many pencils fit in a pencil box? How many boxes would you need to hold 1,000 pencils? How many pages are in a spiral notebook?*

Hold a brief class discussion for members of each group to share some of their examples and the reasoning behind their choices. Encourage students to question each other's examples, if appropriate, and explain why they do not agree with a given example.

Continue the lesson by using an overhead projector and base ten blocks to model 1,000. Write the number 1,000 on the overhead. Have students name the places from the ones place through the thousands place. Discuss with students the relationship between the ones place and the tens place, the tens place and the hundreds place, and finally the hundreds place and the thousands place. Encourage them to generalize that as they move left, each place is 10 times greater than the previous place. Have students determine how many of each place it would take to make 1,000; that is, 1,000 ones, 100 tens, 10 hundreds, or 1 thousand.

f.y.i.

Help students see that sometimes addition or subtraction causes the number in any of the places to become greater than 9. Point out that this automatically changes the number in the place to the left. Have students use calculators and input "998." Tell them to add "1" twice to see how the number "998" becomes "999" and then "1,000." Discuss with students why the first "1" did not change the number in any place except the ones column. Have students describe what happened when the second "1" was added and why.

DISTRIBUTE STUDENT PAGE 22 and sets of base ten blocks. Have students work in small groups to complete the tables on student page 22. Encourage each group to give the tables they create to another group to solve. When each group has completed the page, hold a brief class discussion. Group members can take turns explaining how they completed the first table. Encourage students to listen to the strategies used, ask questions about them, and think about their own strategies during this discussion.

What Might Happen . . . What to Do

Some students might get confused about the relationship between the value places in our number system. Focus on relationships they already know and understand. For example, there are 10 ones/units in one ten. So, 1 ten = 10 × 1. Using this format, build up to the thousands place, each time writing a multiplication sentence.

Spend the rest of the lesson having students estimate addends and subtrahends other than 1, 10, or 100 to get sums and differences that equal 1,000. For example, ask students what they would add to 250 to get 1,000. *What would you subtract from 1,375 to get 1,000?* Have students discuss how they determined the missing addends or subtrahends. Give additional problems such as $374 + ? \approx 1{,}000$ and $1{,}317 - ? \approx 1{,}000$. Remind them that when using estimation, they do not have to find an exact answer.

Extension

Have students continue the activity to 10,000. Encourage them to write about the relationship that exists between the thousands place and the ten thousands place. Have them discuss how many thousands are in 10,000 and what fraction 1,000 is of 10,000.

Student Pages

Student page 22 has place value charts that are used during the lesson. Student page 23 contains practice items in which students choose from three choices to get a sum or difference close to 1,000 or estimate the number that best completes the number sentence.

Assessment

As students worked on activities estimating physical quantities, you observed students' initial sense of the magnitude of 1,000. As you listened to them relate the strategies they used to devise their initial examples of what constitutes 1,000, you got a good idea of their sense of number. Listening, observing, and careful directed questioning also helped you see how students reasoned through the relationships between the value places in the number system.

NCTM Standards Summary

During this lesson, students used communication to share their sense of number quantity, to relate and discuss their strategies for estimating and representing the quantity, and to discuss place value. They used representation and reasoning and proof as they found examples of everyday things that represented 1,000 or more. They used base ten blocks to represent place value in exploring the relationships between ones, tens, hundreds, and thousands. They also used reasoning and proof to determine and test the rule about the relationships between number place values as "times 10" moving from right to left.

Answers

Page 22

Row 1. 5 hundreds
Row 2. 60 tens
Row 3. 1,000 ones

Page 23

1. 350
2. 273
3. 190
4. 1,001
5. 501
6. 2,100
7. 537 + 463
   124 + 876
   609 + 391
   994 + 6
8. Any answer from 151–349.
9. Any answer from 332–530.
10. Any answer from 568–766.
11. Any answer from 1,173–1,271.
12. Answers will vary.
13. 20 minutes
14. Fewer than 300.

Name

Recognizing 1,000

Complete the table. Build 1,000 in each row by telling what the question mark stands for.

thousands	hundreds	tens	ones
	?	50	
	4	?	
			?

Make your own puzzles. Build 1,000. Have other classmates tell what your question marks stand for.

thousands	hundreds	tens	ones

Name ______________________

Recognizing 1,000

Write the correct number.

❶ $650 + \_\_\_\_\_\_\_\_ = 1,000$

❷ $1,273 - \_\_\_\_\_\_\_\_ = 1,000$

❸ $810 + \_\_\_\_\_\_\_\_ = 1,000$

❹ $2,001 - \_\_\_\_\_\_\_\_ = 1,000$

❺ $499 + \_\_\_\_\_\_\_\_ = 1,000$

❻ $3,100 - \_\_\_\_\_\_\_\_ = 1,000$

Match the two numbers that when added together equal 1,000.

❼

537	124	609	994
876	391	6	463

Choose a number that makes each statement true. Use estimation or mental math.

❽ $1,000 < 850 + \_\_\_\_\_\_\_\_ < 1200$

❾ $1,000 < 1531 - \_\_\_\_\_\_\_\_ < 1,200$

❿ $900 < 333 + \_\_\_\_\_\_\_\_ < 1100$

⓫ $950 < 2222 - \_\_\_\_\_\_\_\_ < 1,050$

⓬ Pick one of the problems from above and explain how you found the answer.

Solve.

⓭ You are counting to 1,000. It has taken you 2 minutes to count to 100, about how long do you think it will take you to count to 1,000?

⓮ You and two friends together are trying to skip rope 1,000 times. Your first friend skipped 380 times and the next friend skipped 450 times. Will you need to skip more or fewer than 300 times? Tell how you know.

Using Estimation

Introduction

Objective → Students will estimate sums using front-end estimation and rounding.

Context → This lesson comes early in a unit or chapter on multi-digit addition and subtraction of whole numbers. Students have previously used mental math in addition and subtraction. They will continue with addition of multi-digit whole numbers with two or more addends.

NCTM Standards Focus

Having a good grasp of the processes of rounding and estimation helps students quickly evaluate sums and differences in operations with multi-digit whole numbers. Understanding how to use mental math to get a ballpark estimate of the solution to a problem is an important step in learning to solve and check problems quickly and accurately. Often students are not given the opportunity to develop estimation and mental math skills. This standards-based lesson focuses on those skills.

Problem Solving Students use problem-solving strategies to identify how to apply prior knowledge of mental math to new situations. They adapt their methods and strategies to explore front-end estimation and rounding.

Communication Students write, listen, talk, and think about when and how to use estimation strategies in addition. They differentiate the usage of front-end estimation and rounding. They adjust their own strategies when they find others that make more sense and are better suited for the problems they are solving.

Teaching Plan

Materials → Student pages 28–29

TELL STUDENTS THAT THIS MORNING as you were getting ready for math class ink spilled on the paper with the addition problem you had prepared for the class and covered 4 of the digits, leaving only two digits visible.

Pose the following questions to the students to begin a discussion of front-end estimation: *If you could choose, which 4 digits would you choose to have covered? Why?* (The tens and the ones digits. Leaving the digits with the greatest place value uncovered will give you a closer estimate of the sum.) *What is the sum, as best as you can determine?* (600 or greater)

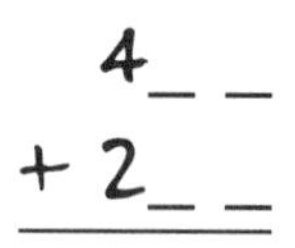

What do you know about this sum? (It cannot be less than 600, since the digits in the hundreds place add up to 600.)
What is the greatest sum possible? (798)

EXPLAIN TO STUDENTS that when you use only the digits in the greatest place, the estimation strategy is called "front-end estimation." Have students discuss the strengths and weaknesses of this method of estimating. Make sure that students discuss the following points about front-end estimation.

- It is a quick way to estimate a sum.
- It is an easy way to get an answer.
- It is almost always less than the actual answer and sometimes it is quite a bit less than the actual answer.

Discuss with students how they could get a better estimate of the sum. Encourage them to begin with front-end estimation, then try adjusting the answer by considering the numbers in the column to the right of the greatest place, in this case the tens.

```
  47_
+ 28_
-----
```

How would you estimate the sum now? Lead the class into a discussion of rounding. Point out that using the tens digits in your estimate leads you to round up. Students should now estimate the sum as 800.

What Might Happen . . . What to Do

Some students might not recall how to round numbers to a specific place value. Spend a few minutes reviewing rounding. Begin with two-digit numbers to establish the rule of 5 or greater. Then move to three-digit numbers. This time establish the rule of 50 or greater.

f.y.i.

Students might offer another possibility. They could use front-end estimation to know the answer must be greater than 600. Adding the 7 tens and the 8 tens gives 15 tens, or 150. Adding this to 600 gives an estimate of 750.

Now present the entire addition problem to the class and ask them how they could estimate the sum more accurately by rounding the addends.

$$\begin{array}{r} 473 \\ +\ 285 \\ \hline \end{array}$$

How would you round the addends? (Round 473 to 500 because it is closer to 500 than to 400. Round 285 to 300 because it is closer to 300 than to 200.) *Now what is your estimate of the sum?* (800) *Is your estimate too high, too low, or about right? How do you know?* (The estimate is too high, because both addends are rounded up to the next hundred.)

Instruct students to write two problems that show one estimate that is too low and one that is about right. Have them write about how each problem is a good example of an estimate that is too low and one that is about right. When they have finished, have them tell how they rounded the numbers and explain their reasoning. Encourage students to listen to each other and to question strategies they do not agree with.

What Might Happen . . . What to Do

Some students might round three-digit numbers to the nearest ten rather than to the nearest hundred. For example, they would round the addends 473 to 470 and 285 to 290. Remind students that an estimate should be an easy way to get an approximate answer. It is easier to add only the hundreds for a quick mental calculation.

Extension

Have students estimate sums of four-digit addend addition problems. Ask them to write about how estimating sums of four-digit numbers is like estimating sums of three-digit numbers.

Student Pages

Student page 28 offers practice with both front-end estimation and rounding. Student page 29 asks students to discuss and compare the two strategies.

Assessment

Throughout the lesson, you had several opportunities to assess students' understanding of the purpose of estimation. You were also able to assess whether they understood front-end estimating and rounding, and whether they were able to evaluate when to use each method. Finally, using the student pages as in-class practice or as homework, allowed you to evaluate how well students have internalized the two estimation strategies and when and how to use them.

NCTM Standards Summary

Students used problem-solving strategies and relied on their prior knowledge in mental math and estimation. They adapted and generalized about estimation and rounding strategies for three-digit numbers. They identified the highest value digits in three-digit numbers and applied them when using front-end estimation. They discussed with each other the strengths and weaknesses of front-end estimation and rounding. They then applied what they were learning to creating and evaluating their own estimation problems as well as solving additional problems requiring estimating strategies. They wrote about their estimation strategies and listened to the strategies of others as they communicated about their methods.

Answers

Page 28

1. Front-end: 900, Rounding: 900
2. Front-end: 700, Rounding: 800
3. Front-end: 900, Rounding: 1000
4. Front-end: 400, Rounding: 400
5. Front-end: 600, Rounding: 600
6. Front-end: 800, Rounding: 1000
7. Front-end: 300, Rounding: 300
8. Front-end: 800, Rounding: 900

Page 29

1. Possible answer: When you use front-end estimation, you use only the digits in the position of the greatest place value to make your estimate. Front-end estimation usually gives a lower answer than the exact answer.
2. Possible answer: In rounding, you look at the digit to the right of the number in the position of greatest place value. You round up if the digit is 5 or greater; down if it is 4 or lower. This method more often gives an estimated answer that is greater than the actual answer. Together with front-end estimation you get a range within which the exact answer falls.

Name

Using Estimation

Estimate the sum using both front-end estimation and rounding.

	Front-end Estimation	Rounding
❶ 445 + 538	900	900
❷ 526 + 278		
❸ 674 + 316		
❹ 332 + 114		
❺ 441 + 219		
❻ 764 + 159		
❼ 219 + 129		
❽ 672 + 226		

Name

Using Estimation

1. Describe front-end estimation.
   What is the strength of front-end estimation?
   What is the weakness of front-end estimation?

2. Describe rounding as an estimation method.
   What is the strength of rounding?
   What is the weakness of rounding?
   How might using it with front-end estimation give you a more accurate answer than either method does alone?

Interpreting Remainders in Division

Introduction

Objective → Students will understand how to calculate and interpret remainders in division.

Context → This lesson generally occurs late in a unit or chapter on division. Students have previously learned division facts and understand division concepts. They will go on to learn the formal division algorithm with multi-digit dividends and one-digit divisors.

NCTM Standards Focus

Often, the process of interpreting remainders and evaluating their significance is grouped with the process of learning the formal division algorithm. However, by having a separate lesson on interpreting remainders that utilizes the following three process standards, students gain a more complete understanding of what a remainder indicates and when the remainder provides information essential to solving a problem.

Reasoning and Proof Students share their thoughts with their groups and the class about how the remainder in a division word problem influences the final solution to that problem. They evaluate and test their own reasoning in evaluating the significance of remainders in given word problems. They listen to and question each other's methods and solutions.

Problem Solving Students use problem-solving strategies to represent and generalize about remainders in division. By analyzing different kinds of division problem situations, students discover on their own what a remainder indicates and when the remainder is an essential part of the solution to a problem.

Representation Students represent, record, and communicate problem situations using pictures. They analyze the representations to determine whether or not the remainder changes the whole number quotient.

Teaching Plan

Materials → Student pages 34–35

HAND OUT STUDENT PAGE 34 and assign students to work in groups of 2 to 4. Explain that they are going to solve four different types of division problems, each of which produces a remainder. They need to decide if and how the remainder changes the answer to the problem. Read the first problem with the class.

Jenny has 35 beads. She is making friendship bracelets for her friends. Each bracelet uses 6 beads. *How many bracelets can she make?*

ASK EACH GROUP TO WRITE DOWN what they know and what they need to find out. Encourage students to use representations and to record the process they use to solve the problem. When they have finished, have a volunteer from each group present the group's solution and explain how they solved the problem and how the remainder influences the quotient.

Methods Students Might Use

- Use a representation such as the following:

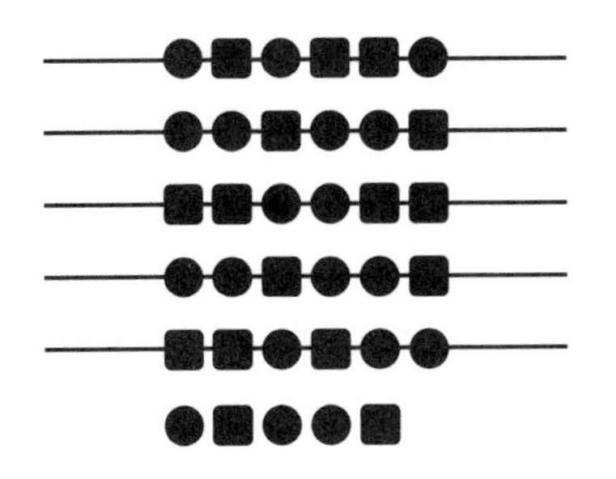

- Use division facts to find that Jenny can make 5 remainder 5 bracelets.

Students should point out that no matter how they solved the problem, the answer is that Jenny can make 5 bracelets. The remainder doesn't influence the solution, because the problem didn't mention using the leftover beads.

> **What Might Happen . . . What to Do**
>
> Some students might make the 5 beads that are left over into a bracelet and give the answer as 6 bracelets. Others who used division facts might give the answer as 5 remainder 5. Ask questions that lead the students to conclude on their own that the remainder plays no role in this problem situation and does not need to be recorded in the answer. Have them use beads or counters to show the number of bracelets with 6 beads that they can make from 35 beads. *How many beads have you used? How many more beads do you have? Can you make one more bracelet with these beads? Why doesn't it matter that there are 5 beads left?*

DIRECT STUDENTS TO SOLVE the next three problems on student page 34. Ask them to discuss each solution in their groups and together determine how the remainder influences their answers. If you have an overhead, give students transparencies so they can write out their representations and strategies before the class discussion.

During the class discussion, have one student from each group present the group's solution and reasoning process. After each presentation, ask the class if they agree or disagree with the process and/or the solution presented or if they have questions to ask the presenters. Make sure that each of the following methods is introduced into the discussion.

Problem 2

Possible Method 1 Represent the problem by drawing 5 vans with 6 students in each van. Five more students are not in a van. Since 5 students can't be left without transportation, a sixth van will have to take those students. The solution is 6 vans.

Possible Method 2 Using division facts, we know that $30 \div 6 = 5$, so at least 5 vans are needed. There are 5 students left. They will fit into 1 more van. Using addition, $5 + 1 = 6$.

Problem 3

Possible Method 1 Use pictures to represent 5 rows with 6 chairs in each row. There are 5 chairs left to go on the stage.

Possible Method 2 Knowing that $30 \div 6 = 5$; subtraction yields $35 - 30 = 5$. This is the remainder, so 5 chairs are put on the stage.

Problem 4

Possible Method 1 Represent the rice-crispy treats as a 5×7 rectangle divided into 35 squares. Shade in 6 treats at a time until there are less than 6 whole treats left. Each kid got 5 whole treats. Now divide each of the 5 leftover treats into 6 smaller pieces. Each kid gets 5 of 6 small pieces, or $\frac{5}{6}$ pieces.

What Might Happen . . . What to Do

Some students might have trouble figuring out how to represent the remainder in Problem 4. If students do not know about representing remainders as fractions, show them that symbolically they can place the remainder over the divisor to show a fraction of a whole. The solution to this problem would be a mixed number, $5\frac{5}{6}$, where the remainder is placed over the divisor and shown as $\frac{5}{6}$. This is probably the most difficult exercise in learning to interpret remainders. If necessary, provide other examples for students. Encourage them to ask questions until they feel comfortable with a quotient showing a mixed number.

Possible Method 2 Use the division process to get $35 \div 6 = 5$ remainder 5. Represent the remainder as the fraction $\frac{5}{6}$. Each kid got $5\frac{5}{6}$ rice crispy treats.

In this lesson, students focused specifically on interpreting and evaluating the significance of remainders. They did this by drawing pictures or using objects to represent the problem or by using symbolic representations of division. In any case, they worked with the same division sentence to determine when a remainder was essential to the answer.

Student Pages

Student page 34 contains the four problems the students solve in class. Student page 35 has more practice division problems requiring students to interpret the significance of the remainder.

Assessment

Since the division sentence $35 \div 6$ was used four times, students focused mainly on what to do with the remainder in each problem situation. The class practice problems gave you the opportunity to observe students' approaches to evaluating remainders. The problems also allowed you to evaluate students' problem-solving and reasoning skills. The practice exercises on student page 35 can be used to provide additional information on students' progress for assessment purposes.

NCTM Standards Summary

Students represented the situations described in each word problem physically or pictorially. They used their problem-solving and reasoning skills to determine how to represent and solve each problem. They divided to find a solution to each problem and then evaluated whether the remainder affected the final solution. Students used class discussion to reason out and explain their problem-solving methods and tell why they worked. They also described the reasoning behind their decisions about using remainders in their final solutions. Finally, students were able to use other students' questions and explanations to adjust and refine their own methods.

Answers

Page 34

1. 5 bracelets
2. 6 minivans
3. 5 rows for the audience and 5 chairs on the stage, or 5 remainder 5
4. $5\frac{5}{6}$ rice-crispy treats

Page 35

1. 5 pages
2. 9 teams with 5 students and 1 team with 4 students; 10 teams total
3. $5\frac{4}{8}$ or $5\frac{1}{2}$
4. Joel had 31 CDs. This problem could be represented as the following division sentence: $31 \div 4 = 7$ remainder 3.
5. $50 \div 6 = 8$ remainder 2. Since the juice cartons come in 6-packs, Luis must buy 9 packs to have enough.
6. Each player will get 10 cards and there will be 2 cards left over.
7. Answers will vary.

Name

Interpreting Remainders in Division

Use division to solve each problem. Show your work. Explain how you used the remainder in each problem.

1. Jenny has 35 beads and is making friendship bracelets for her friends. Each bracelet uses 6 beads. How many bracelets can she make?

2. Some fourth grade students are going to the Statue of Liberty on a field trip. There are 35 students going on the trip. They will travel in minivans. Each minivan holds 6 students. How many minivans will they need?

3. For the class play, Lena and Mickey are arranging 35 chairs in rows of 6 for the audience. They placed the remaining chairs on the stage. How many rows did they make? How many chairs are on the stage?

4. For Erik's party, his mom made 35 rice-crispy treats. Including Erik, there are 6 kids at the party. They share all the treats equally. How many treats did each kid get?

Name

Interpreting Remainders in Division

Solve the problems. Show your work.
Explain how you used the remainder in each problem.

1. Annette got a package of 45 sports cards. She put them in her card album. Each page holds 8 cards. How many pages did she fill completely?

2. There are 49 students participating in Sports Day. The principal divides the students into teams. If each team can have no more than 5 students, what is the smallest number of teams the principal can make?

3. Yolanda is making bread. The recipe calls for 44 ounces of water. She is using an 8-ounce measuring cup. How many cups will she measure?

4. Joel organized his CDs into 4 cases. Each case held 7 CDs. Joel had 3 CDs left over. How many CDs did Joel have to begin with? How could you represent this problem as a division sentence?

5. Juice cartons come in packs of 6. Luis needs 50 juice cartons. How many packs must he buy?

6. There are 52 cards in a deck. Kendra and 4 of her friends are playing a card game. Kendra dealt the same number of cards to each player. How many cards did each player get? How many cards were left over?

7. Choose one of the word problems above. Write about how you solved the problem. Tell whether and how you used the remainder in your solution and explain why you made these choices.

Subtracting Across Zeros

Introduction

Objective → Students will accurately subtract multi-digit numbers in which the minuend—the number being subtracted from—has two or more consecutive zeros.

Context → Students have subtracted numbers through the thousands with regrouping. They have subtracted from numbers with single zeros but not several consecutive zeros. This lesson comes at the end of a unit on subtraction.

Subtracting Across Zeros

Learn

The stadium can hold 4,000 people. There are 2,435 people at the stadium today. How many more people could it hold?

4,000 – 2,435 = ____

Estimate: 4,000 – 2,000 = 2,000

Step 1
There are no ones, tens, or hundreds to subtract. Let's regroup 1 thousand as 10 hundreds.

```
 3 10
 4,000
-2,435
```

Step 2
Regroup 1 hundred as 10 tens.

```
    9
 3 1010
 4,000
-2,435
```

Step 3
Regroup 1 ten as 10 ones.

```
    9 9
 3 101010
 4,000
-2,435
```

Step 4
Subtract.

```
    9 9
 3 101010
 4,000
-2,435
 1,565
```

The stadium can hold 1,565 more people.

Explore

Subtract.

A. 700 – 109

B. 6,000 – 2,513

C. 8,000 – 6,914

NCTM Process Standards Analysis and Focus

The standards analysis examines how the process standards have been incorporated into the above lesson. By increasing the focus on three of the process standards, a more effective and meaningful lesson can be presented. The suggestions offered can help you to think about how this might be accomplished.

Connections While a connection to estimation is made in the example problem, estimation is not used in the lesson. A connection to regrouping in subtraction is modeled in the example.

Suggestion → **Students already know how to perform subtraction with regrouping when they come to this special case in subtraction. Making connections between subtraction**

Try

Subtract.

1.	900 − 365	**2.**	6,000 − 2,355	**3**	9,000 − 658	**4.**	5,000 − 1,673	**5.**	60,805 − 43,632
6.	400 − 230	**7.**	703 − 478	**8.**	900 − 607	**9.**	530 − 87	**10.**	800 − 560
11.	7,080 − 3,260	**12.**	4,000 − 2,250	**13.**	6,600 − 542	**14.**	9,000 − 6,892	**15.**	5,000 − 2,053
16.	60,070 − 36,754	**17.**	89,000 − 36,891	**18.**	30,009 − 10,438	**19.**	60,085 − 5,963	**20.**	70,800 − 42,680

Word Problems

21. John's store received an order of 3,000 boxes of paper clips. He needs to keep 1,543 boxes and send the rest to another store. How many boxes should he send to the other store?

22. Harold has read 335 pages of 1,000 page book. How many pages does he have left to read if he is to finish the book?

23. Tara is working with a group of people who are checking a computer program for a bug. There are 2,173 lines of code in the program. They have checked 893 lines. If they check all the lines on the program, how many more lines do they have to check?

problems they know how to solve and subtracting from numbers with multiple zeros will help students understand that the same procedures apply.

Reasoning and Proof This lesson does not require that students use reasoning or explain their thinking. However, this is the only opportunity offered for students to think about how the numbers in the problem affect regrouping.

Suggestion → **Reasoning is essential to build understanding of the way regrouping works across multiple zeros. Asking students to review existing knowledge of subtraction by explaining their thinking as they solve problems will help them see the consistency in procedures used in different types of problems.**

Representation The example at the beginning of the lesson shows the record of the regrouping that was done for the completed problem.

Suggestion → **Having students focus on place value and explain how they regroup will help them understand why it is important to account for each column. Students will also see how recording each step helps them keep track and results in greater accuracy.**

Problem Solving Problem solving consists of several word problems requiring subtraction across zeros.

Communication Opportunities for communication are limited to a single discussion question.

The teaching plan that follows shows how the suggestions for increasing the focus on the process standards can be implemented.

Revised Teaching Plan

BEGIN THE LESSON BY ACTIVATING STUDENTS' EXISTING knowledge of multi-digit subtraction. Pose the problem 360 − 168 and ask students to solve it individually. Ask them to go slowly and carefully and notice the steps they are using to solve the problem. It's helpful to ask students to be extra thorough in showing their work on paper. *Even though you know how to do this problem and could do it quickly, I want you to go slowly and show your work. We're going to look at some challenging subtraction problems today, and it will help us to really pay attention to what we already know about subtracting.*

f.y.i.

In this lesson, the number being subtracted from is referred to as the minuend.

Allow time for students to examine the problem. Work it on the board step-by-step with student help. Call on different students to tell you what each step is. Asking *Why do we do that?* and other reasoning questions will help students make connections and clarify the thinking they use to solve problems.

Be sure students are comfortable with these initial problems before continuing. We are using these two- and three-digit problems with single zeros in the minuend as a bridge to understanding three- and four-digit problems with multiple zeros. Be on the alert for students who are just "going through the steps" without showing an understanding of place value. *"You just write a little one there"* is a red flag; whereas *"you trade one of the 6 tens to make 10 ones"* is the kind of mathematical reasoning that will support students in thinking flexibly and clearly about computation.

NEXT, POSE A PAIR OF PROBLEMS such as 333 − 217 and 303 − 217 to illustrate changes that occur when subtracting across a zero in the minuend. Give students time to work through these problems, and ask them to pay attention to the effect the zero in the tens place of 303 has. As students work, circulate and ask additional *why* questions of students you haven't heard from yet. In all of your assessments in this lesson, focus on whether students have really understood that regrouping is a simple rearrangement based on the base-ten number system.

As you discuss this pair of problems, give emphasis to the fact that though the regrouping moves across a zero in the second problem, the process is really the same. This is an essential bridge to connect existing student knowledge about subtraction with problems containing multiple zeros in this lesson. If needed, pose a few more pairs of subtraction problems such as 132 – 47 and 102 – 47 for students to solve and discuss.

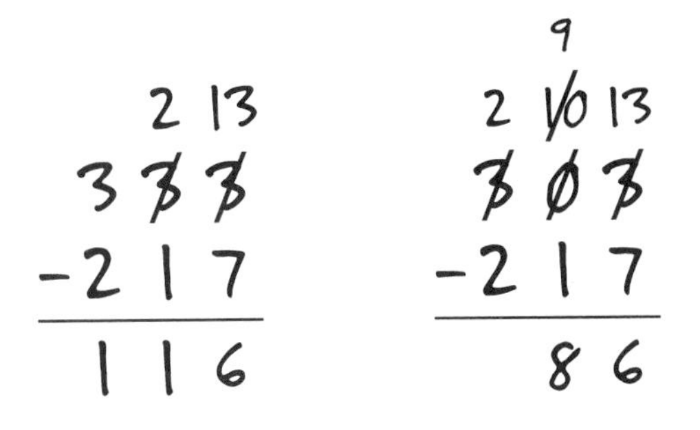

TAKE THE NEXT STEP by asking students to work the problem 500 – 167. Ask questions that will help students make connections between regrouping in the previous problems and this situation with two adjacent zeros. *How is this problem similar to the problems we just did? How is this problem different?* Refer back to the specific steps in previous problems. *When we did 360 – 168, how did we handle subtracting the 8 in the ones place? In 303 – 217, when we needed more ones to subtract the 7 in the ones place, what did we do? Why?*

Discuss each problem and model carefully recording the steps of regrouping one column at a time. Explain how this representation confirms that the value of the minuend is not changing. Insist students do this recording in their work. Point out that neatness and accuracy in recording each step are particularly important with the multi-step regroupings that occur when minuends contain multiple zeros. *When I regroup one of the hundreds to make 10 tens, has the value of the number we are working with changed? When we regroup, have we taken any away yet?*

NEXT, WRITE 3,000 – 1,675 ON THE BOARD and ask students to find the difference. Remind them that the steps of regrouping work equally well with any subtraction problem, and reemphasize the importance of recording each step carefully. Work the problem on the board after students are finished. Put the digits in a place-value chart as shown as another way to represent the regrouping process. Emphasize the connections to previous problems.

...	1000s	100s	10s	1s . .
		9	9	
	2	~~10~~	~~10~~	10
	~~3~~	~~0~~	~~0~~	~~0~~
−	1	6	7	5

Pair students and have them work together to complete several more problems containing multiple zeros in the minuend. Include a five-digit number if students seem comfortable. Consider having students split up the problems, work independently, and then discuss their answers and methods with each other. A good way to build in accountability and check understanding is to ask students to explain one of the problems their partners solved to you or the class.

Engage the class in this enjoyable activity. To represent the regrouping process in a more concrete way, ask four students to line up and have each hold a large name tag to designate the thousands, hundreds, tens, or ones place. Tell the thousands student that he/she can handle only thousand dollar bills, the hundreds student only hundred dollar bills, and so on. Using play money, give the thousands student five bills and ask how much money the group has ($5,000). Pose the problem 5,000 − 3,589, and tell the group they want to buy a used car for $3,589 and the dealer doesn't have any change.

Do we have 9 ones to give the car dealer? How will the ones student get some ones? The physical trading required by having the thousands student exchange 1 thousand for 10 hundreds and hand them to the hundreds student models the mathematics of regrouping in subtraction in a visible and interactive way. This activity also makes clear that skipping over the zeros doesn't make sense in regrouping: the thousands student can see that it isn't practical to exchange one of the thousands for a thousand ones!

Follow up the above activity by writing the problem on the chalkboard and going over the steps again to reinforce the connection between the concrete and symbolic representation forms.

As a closing activity, pose the following questions: *How would you explain to a friend what to do when finding 4,005 − 2,017? What is the most important thing your friend should remember?* Answering these questions will help students review the steps and focus on the reasoning involved in this procedure. You can use these questions for discussion or assign them to the pairs as a written exercise.

Student Pages

Students are now ready to complete practice exercises similar to those shown on the reduced student pages.

Assessment

Having students describe the steps they used as they worked through a subtraction problem provided an opportunity to check their understanding of the regrouping process. As they played the money exchange game, you could assess their understanding of how regrouping relates to our place-value system.

NCTM Standards Summary

Students reviewed connections between the familiar procedure of regrouping or renaming and our place-value system. By reasoning through the steps used to subtract, they extended that knowledge to subtraction problems with multiple zeros. By emphasizing the written representation of this mathematical procedure, students were better able to keep track of their steps and were made aware that regrouping does not change the value of the minuend.

Standard 2 **Algebra**

At the fourth grade level, algebra includes a lot of work with multiplication and division, the coordinate system, functions, equations, and variables. Our lessons are derived from these important topics. They include a lesson on understanding variables, a lesson on making equivalent equations, a lesson on ordered pairs on a coordinate grid, and a lesson on the properties of multiplication.

Three lessons model how the process standards can be used to teach content. A fourth lesson is a hypothetical textbook lesson that we have revised to be more standards based. These four lessons do not represent the entire curriculum, but rather provide glimpses of how, with a more concentrated effort to incorporate the process standards, better mathematics teaching and learning can be achieved.

One lesson we have chosen focuses on opposite, or inverse, functions. By incorporating the process standards of representation, reasoning and proof, and communication, a lesson can be presented in which tables are used to show functions and their inverses.

© Creative Publications

Students generalize from these the rules for determining inverses, and students will find an input, given a function and an output.

In another lesson we have chosen, students will identify rules for composite, or two-step, functions. The process standards of reasoning and proof, representation, and communication drive this lesson, as students determine the one-step or two-step operations that relate inputs with their outputs.

A third lesson we have chosen focuses on writing and graphing ordered pairs on a coordinate plane. Instead of working with random points, students use the process standards of reasoning and proof and communication to identify patterns formed by ordered pairs and by points on a coordinate grid. They predict additional ordered pairs and then verify their predictions.

The hypothetical textbook lesson we have chosen to revise is one that focuses on the four properties of multiplication. Through better incorporation of the process standards of reasoning and proof, communication, and representation, students will try to disprove the commutative property, the associative property, the property of one, and the zero property, all for multiplication.

Standard 2 Lessons

Understanding Opposite Functions

Using Two-Step Functions

Exploring Ordered Pairs

Discovering the Properties of Multiplication

Understanding Opposite Functions

Introduction

Objective → Given a function, students will determine the inverse, or opposite, function.

Context → Students are familiar with related operations from their work with basic facts. They have learned about function rules and found outputs for given inputs. After students understand the concept of opposite operations and can work back and forth with all four operations, they will go on to use variables and solve simple equations.

NCTM Standards Focus

Students who understand the relationships between addition and subtraction and multiplication and division will be prepared for later work with variables and equations. By using tables and charts to explore inverse functions, students will become proficient at identifying paired operations and, in the case of composite functions, the order in which the operations are performed. In this standards-based lesson, students will develop insight into the mathematical concepts of inverses and identity.

Representation Students will use charts and tables to represent functions and their opposites.

Reasoning and Proof Students will generalize rules for determining inverses of functions. Given an output and the function rule, students will use reasoning to identify the input.

Communication Students will explain inverse relationships in real-world and mathematical situations. They will report their conclusions about one- and two-step functions both orally and in writing.

Teaching Plan

Materials → Student pages 48–49

BEGIN THE LESSON by describing some real-life situations in which a change of condition occurs and have students focus on what is necessary to restore the condition to its original state. *Suppose you collected $5 from each student in the class for a trip. If the trip were cancelled, how would you refund the money?* (Give $5 back to each student.) *If your puppy was sick and lost 2 pounds, what would have to happen for the puppy to return to its original weight?* (It would have to gain or add 2 pounds.) Encourage students to offer some examples of their own, in which they describe a change and what to do to return to the starting point.

Briefly review basic concepts involved with functions, explaining that operations may be described in terms of a machine with three main parts—an input or beginning number; a rule that tells what to do to the input; and an output, which is the number that results from using the rule. Remind students that for each input, there is only one output.

Draw a flowchart on the board to represent the general steps of a function. Draw two additional charts, one with the rule "add 6," and the other with the rule "multiply by 3," both with inputs and outputs. Work through the examples with students and then offer students more practice by asking them to give the outputs for other inputs with each rule.

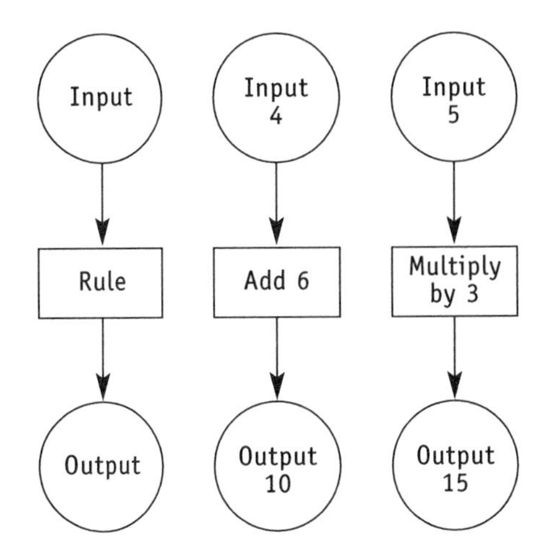

Ask students to imagine that the machine could be made to run in reverse from output to input. Draw a related figure for each chart and emphasize the direction of the operation.

Focus on the pair of charts with the rule "add 6." *What rule should replace the question mark?* (Subtract 6.) *Why did you choose that rule?* (Because the opposite of adding 6 is subtracting 6.) *How can we prove the rule is correct?* (Start with 10, subtract 6, you end with 4.) Restate the relationship by telling students that subtracting 6 "undoes" adding 6.

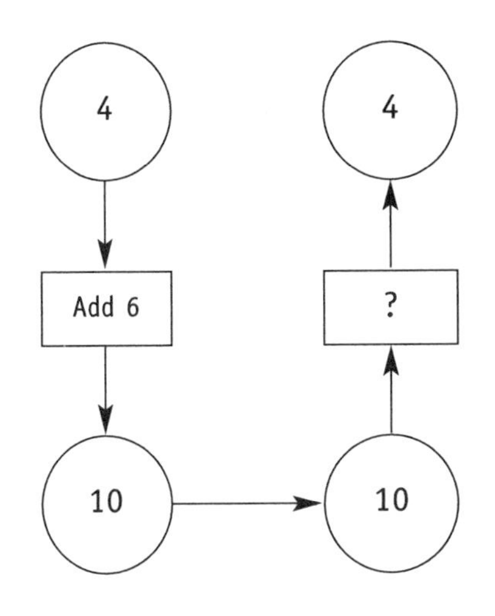

Direct students' attention to the pair of charts containing the rule "multiply by 3." *What rule should replace the question mark for this function?* (Divide by 3.) *Why did you choose that rule?* (Because the opposite of multiplying by 3 is dividing by 3; division "undoes" multiplication.) *How can we show that the rule is correct?* ($15 \div 3 = 5$)

Reinforce students' understanding of using opposite operations by asking them to state the opposite rule for specific operations.

- *Subtract 7.* (Add 7.)
- *Divide by 4.* (Multiply by 4.)
- *Add 10.* (Subtract 10.)
- *Multiply by 8.* (Divide by 8.)
- *Double a number.* (Halve the number or divide by the number by 2.)
- *Decrease a number by 1.* (Increase the number by 1.)

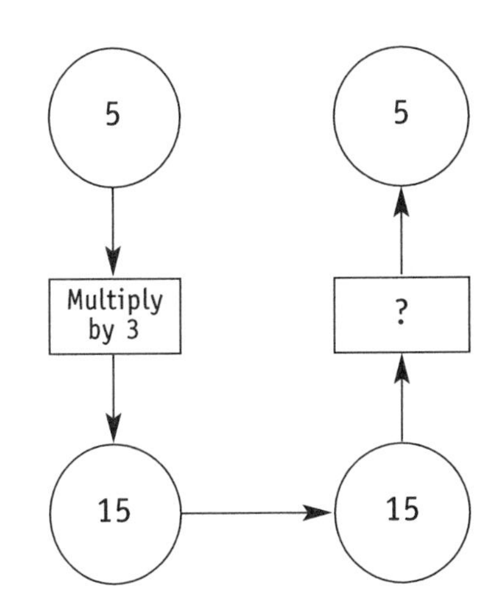

Have students explain a general method for determining the rules for opposite functions either orally or in writing. Students should explain that addition and subtraction are opposites and multiplication and division are opposite operations.

f.y.i.

If your students do not yet know patterns for dividing by 10, a simpler table using basic facts may be substituted.

NEXT, PRESENT FUNCTION TABLES rather than charts to help students extend their understanding of opposite functions to a more abstract level. Write the tables shown here on the board and have students copy them. Be sure to leave the input columns blank as you write the tables on the board.

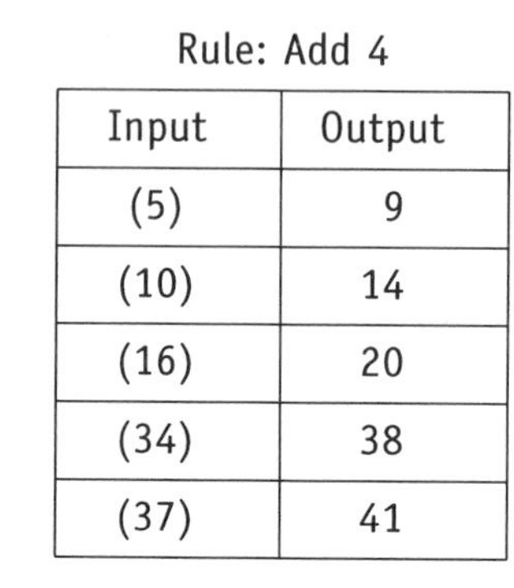

Rule: Add 4

Input	Output
(5)	9
(10)	14
(16)	20
(34)	38
(37)	41

Rule: Multiply by 10

Input	Output
(2)	20
(10)	100
(18)	180
(25)	250
(33)	330

Have students work individually or in pairs to determine the rules that will allow them to find the input for each given output, and then use the rules to complete each of the tables. Allow about 5 minutes for students to work, then have them discuss their answers and explain their reasoning. *What opposite rule did you use for the chart with the rule "add 4?"* (Subtract 4.) *How can you check to see that the numbers you placed in the input column are correct?* (Use the rule to add 4 to each amount in the input column and compare result with the amount in the output column.) *What opposite rule did you use for the cart with the rule "multiply by 10?"* (Divide by 10.) *How can you check to see if the numbers you wrote in the input column are correct?* (Multiply them by 10 and compare with given outputs.)

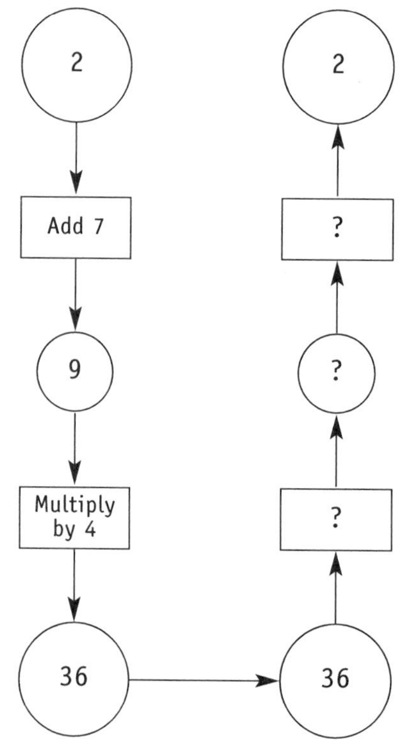

CONCLUDE THE LESSON by having students analyze problems involving two-step, or composite functions. Begin with a paired chart and have students determine the missing rules.

Instruct students to give the opposite rules to be used at each step and emphasize that the operations are "undone" in reverse order. First the multiplication must be undone by dividing by 4, and then the addition must be undone by subtracting 7.

Next, have students analyze two-step tables. As you write a table on the board, be sure to leave the input column blank. Have students determine the opposite rules and then work backward from the given outputs to find

the corresponding inputs. Ask students to explain their reasoning and how they can check their answers.

Input	(Multiply by 2) Divide by 2	(Add 5) Subtract 5	Output
(18)			4
(28)			9
(50)			20

Extension

Instruct students to construct a chart for some "function" or activity in their daily lives that involves 2–5 steps. Then have them construct the chart showing the opposite steps to get back to the starting point.

Student Pages

On student page 48, students use charts containing a rule and outputs and work backward to find the input. On student page 49, students use tables to determine opposite rules and inputs from the information provided. Exercises involving two-step functions are included.

Assessment

It was possible to assess students' informal ideas about opposite functions as they suggested real-life examples. When they discussed the charts and tables and explained how to find rules and inputs, it was possible evaluate their understanding of inverses and operations as well as their proficiency with computations. Noting students who were able to extend their thinking to two-step functions was also possible then.

NCTM Standards Summary

Displaying paired charts helped students reason through the steps involved in reversing functions and generalizing their ideas about pairs of opposite functions. The visual support offered by representing information in flowcharts and tables enabled students to develop insight into the operations performed. Class discussions provided opportunities to communicate their understanding of opposite operations and explain their thinking as students worked through the process of reversing functions.

Answers

Page 48

1. Add 12.
2. Multiply by 8.
3. Subtract 19.
4. Divide by 20.
5. Input 6; divide by 7.
6. Input 43; add 8.
7. Input 27; subtract 13.
8. Input 75; multiply by 5.
9. 21, 27; multiply by 3.
10. 7, 9; divide by 3.

The tables show opposite functions. When you use the function and follow it by its opposite, the result is the original starting number.

Page 49

1. 16, 40, 48, 72; multiply by 8.
2. 19, 48, 70, 103; subtract 10.
3. 14, 19, 32, 48; add 7.
4. 3, 5, 7, 10; divide by 9.
5. Input 3; divide by 2, Subtract 3.
6. Input 26; multiply by 3, add 5.
7. Input 45; divide by 4, multiply by 5.
8. Input 8; subtract 20, divide by 6.
9. The opposite rule would be *Divide by 1.*
10. For both rules, all of the inputs and outputs would be the same.
11. The rule *Add 0* and the opposite rule *Subtract 0* would give the same result.

Name ________________________________

Understanding Opposite Functions

Write the opposite.

1. Subtract 12. ______________________
2. Divide by 8. ______________________
3. Add 19. ______________________
4. Multiply by 20. ______________________

For 5–8, fill in the input. Write the opposite rule that you used.

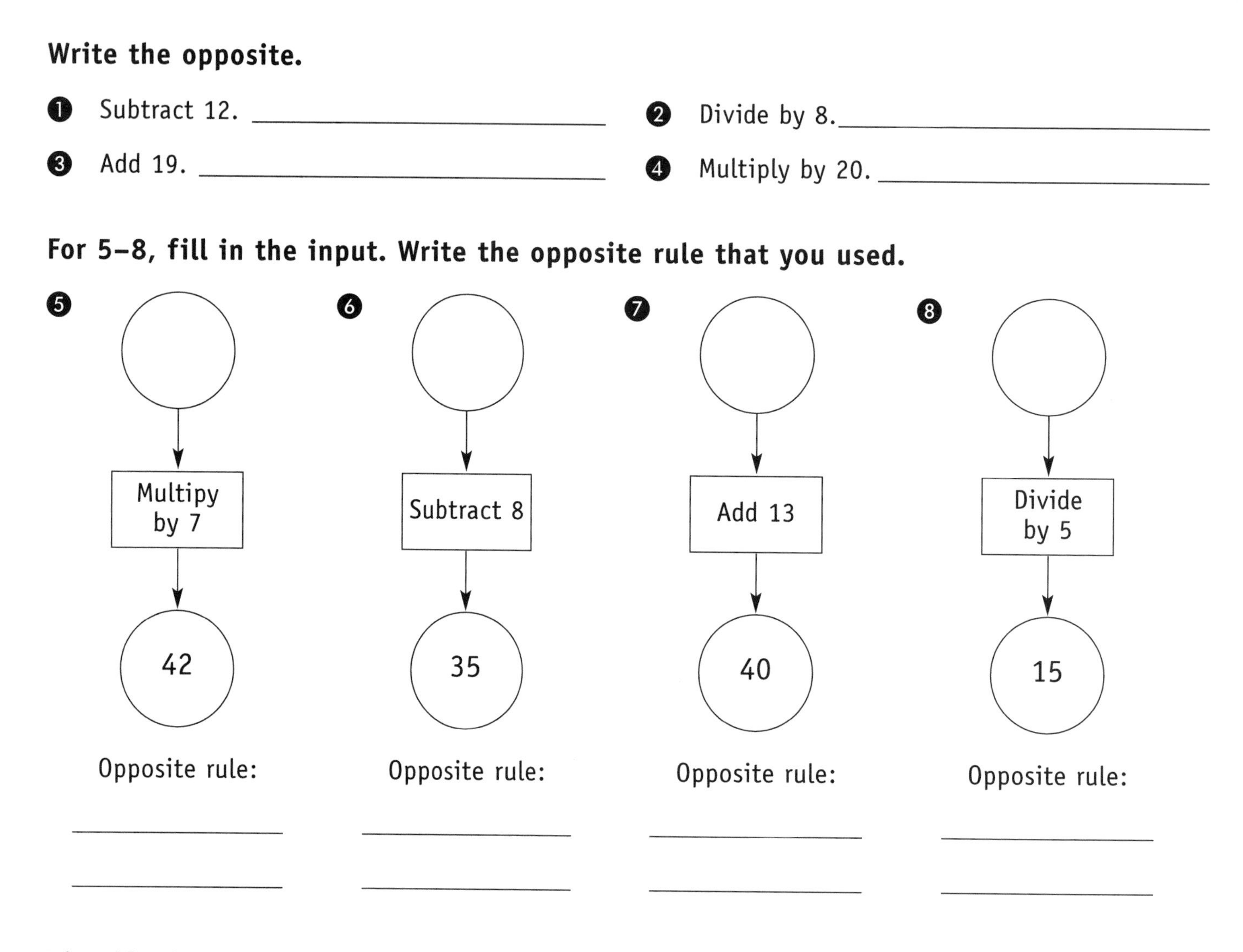

Opposite rule: ______________ ______________

Opposite rule: ______________ ______________

Opposite rule: ______________ ______________

Opposite rule: ______________ ______________

Identify the rule for each function table and complete the table. Then explain the relationship between the two tables.

9. Rule: ______________

Input	Output
1	3
4	12
6	18
7	
9	

10. Rule: ______________

Input	Output
3	1
12	4
18	6
21	
27	

Name

Understanding Opposite Functions

Complete each table. Find the input for each output. Write the opposite rule you used below the table.

1. Rule: Divide by 8.

Input	Output
	2
	5
	6
	9

Rule: ____________

2. Rule: Add 10.

Input	Output
	29
	58
	80
	113

Rule: ____________

3. Rule: Subtract 7.

Input	Output
	7
	12
	25
	41

Rule: ____________

4. Rule: Multiply by 9.

Input	Output
	27
	45
	63
	90

Rule: ____________

For 5–8, find the input for each output. Explain the steps you used.

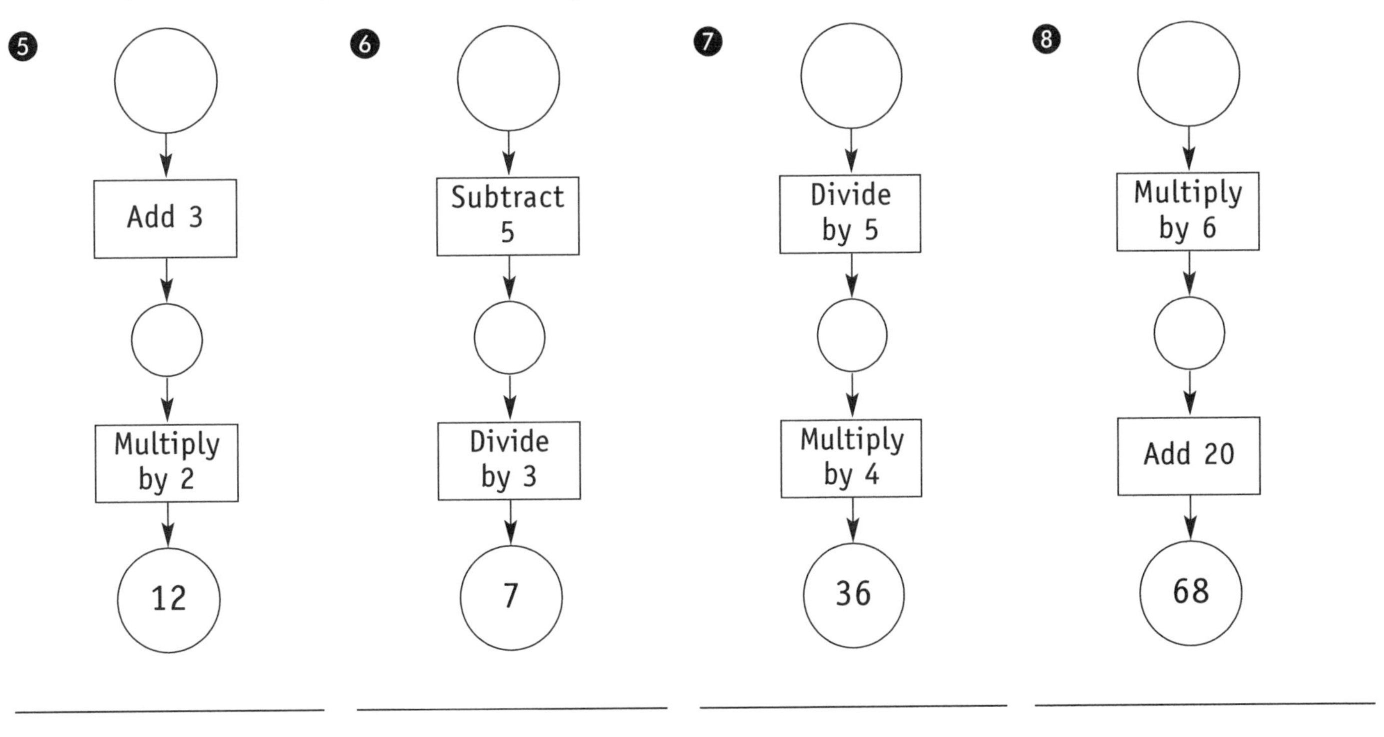

9. Suppose you are given the rule "Multiply by 1." What is the opposite rule?

10. Describe the inputs and the outputs you would have for question 9.

11. Write a different pair of opposite function rules that would give the same result.

Using Two-Step Functions

Introduction

Objective → Students will identify rules for composite (two-step) functions.

Context → Students have determined outputs for simple functions and have identified function rules. This lesson lays the foundation for future work with inverse functions, using function rules to analyze patterns, and writing expressions with variables.

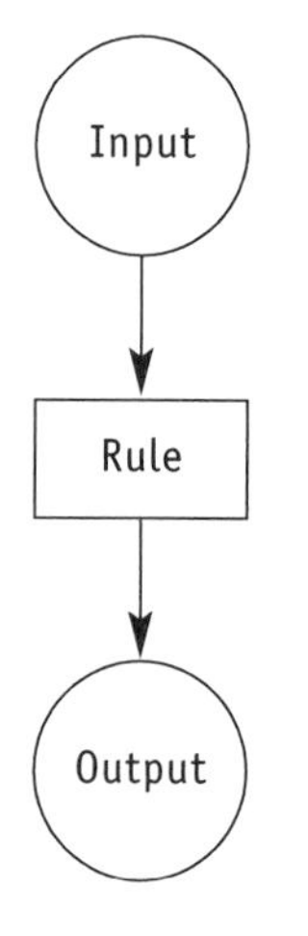

NCTM Standards Focus

In this standards-based lesson, students will investigate simple and composite functions. They will focus on rules that change a given input into a given output, and they will understand that once the rules are established, the output depends only on the input number. This focus will reinforce the basic principle of a function having exactly one output for a given input. As they work with functions, students will be using the concept of identifying unknown numbers in preparation for later work with variables.

Reasoning and Proof Students will use reasoning to identify function rules based on given inputs and outputs. They will determine one-step and possible two-step operations that relate inputs and outputs and will explain and justify the rules they create.

Representation Students will use flowcharts and tables that represent one-and two-step functions to determine the rules being applied. They will describe those rules verbally and represent them in written form.

Communication As students discuss the rules they found and describe the strategies they used both verbally and in written form, they will communicate and clarify their understanding of functions.

Teaching Plan

Materials → Student pages 54–55

BEGIN THE LESSON with a brief review of simple functions. Explain that a function can be thought of as a machine with three parts—an *input* or starting number; a rule that tells what to do to the input; and an *output*, which is the number that results from using the rule. Illustrate this concept by drawing a flowchart to represent a function machine on the board.

Provide students with practice in using functions and finding outputs.

- *The machine is using the rule* add 4. *If the input number is 3, what is the output number?* (7)
- *Are any other output numbers possible?* (No.)
- *If the rule were* multiply by 6 *and the input was 5, what would the output be?* (30)

Rule ?

Input	Output
9	2
12	5
16	9
20	13
25	?

DISPLAY THE TABLE on the board or overhead. Ask students to study the table to determine the rule being applied and to identify the missing number.

What rule is the function machine using? (Subtract 7.) *How do you know the rule is subtraction?* (Students may suggest that since the output numbers were less than the input, they thought of subtraction and recognized the first few input/output pairs from basic facts.) *What is the missing output?* (18)

Present another situation for students to consider. *At Beth's Bargain Books, all books cost $4 each. This week the store is celebrating its third year in business, so Beth is giving a $3 discount on everyone's total purchase. Let's see what happens when a customer comes to the cash register with 6 books.*

DRAW A FLOWCHART to represent a function machine on the board or overhead, and work with students to fill in the missing amounts.

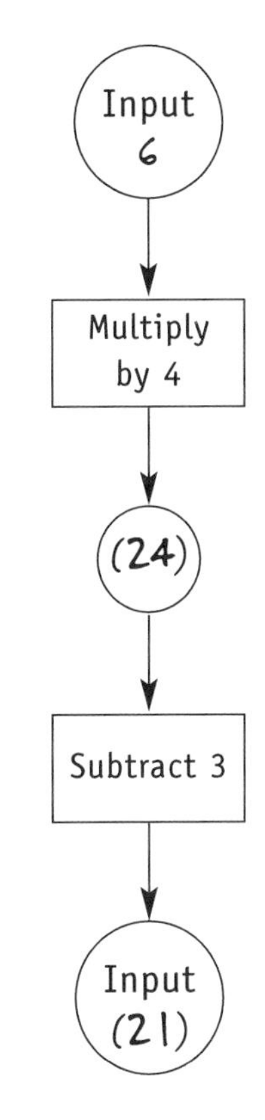

What is the input for this function? (The number of books; 6) Be sure all students understand that if the machine has the rules entered into it, once the input number is given, all that has to be done is to calculate the output. Walk students through each step. *What is the first rule that the machine uses?* (Multiply by 4.) *What is the output for this first step?* (24) *What is the input for the second part of this rule?* (The output just found, 24) *What is the second part of the rule?* (Subtract 3.) *What is the final output? What does the final output represent?* (21; $21 is the final cost for 6 books.) Emphasize that in this situation, cost is a function of the number of books.

Guide students to work through another example. *Suppose a customer came to the register with 8 books. Explain how the machine would find the amount the customer must pay.* (Input 8, $4 \times 8 = 32$, $32 - 3 = 29$, output final cost of $29.) *Is $29 the only possible output for an input of 8 books?* (Yes.) Point out that students have used a two-step function with this example.

Draw attention to the fact that students were able to figure out one-step function rules by examining several input/output pairs. Explain that now, they will try to find two-step rules.

Rule ?

Input	Output
2	5
3	7
5	11
7	15
8	?
10	?

WRITE THE TABLE on the board. Instruct students to work individually or in pairs to determine a two-step rule that would produce the input/output pairs in the table. Tell students to use their rules to calculate the missing outputs. Allow students about 5 minutes to work on the problem, then have them discuss their answers. *What operations did you try? Why?* (Students might explain that they tried various additions and multiplications because the outputs were greater than the inputs.) *What rules did you decide on?* (Multiply by 2; add 1.) *What is the output for 8?* (17) *For 10?* (21).

Have students analyze another example. Make sure they understand that a two-step rule is being used. Begin by giving only one input/output pair for students to consider, but advise students that after they have worked with this pair for a couple of minutes, they will be given another input/output pair to help them confirm the rules.

Input 2 → Output 10

What rules might work here? (Possible answers include add 3, multiply by 2; multiply by 4, add 2; multiply by 6, subtract 2; multiply by 3, add 4; and so on.) If students suggest "multiply by 5" or "add 8," remind them they must use two steps. *Is one input/output pair enough to find out what is being done?* (No.)

Provide a second input/output pair.

Input 3 → Output 14

How can you use this new information to help you find the rules? Explain your strategy. (Students should articulate that applying the rules they came up with for the first input/output pair to the input for the second pair should help them determine which rules produce the correct output.) Ask students if there are any other input/output pairs they would like to try. If no student asks for the input/output for zero, suggest that knowing the output for zero can provide a great deal of information.

Input 0 → Output 2

How can knowing the output for zero help you find the rules? (Since any number times 0, is 0, and the output is 2 greater than the input, a number was added.) *Do you have enough information to state the rules now?* (Most students should be able to identify the steps as "multiply by 4, add 2.") *Use this two-step rule to find the output for an input of 5.* (22)

Conclude the lesson by having students create a two-step function and write clues by writing input/output pairs for their function. Have pairs of students trade their clues and try to identify the rules for the functions.

f.y.i.

Note that since negative numbers are not used at this level, a number less than zero should not be shown for an output of 0.

Extension

Have students work with functions that use inputs of more than one number.

Input 5 and 6. Add the numbers (11); multiply by 2 (22).

Input 3 and 5. Multiply the numbers (15); subtract 6 (9).

Student Pages

Student page 54 offers practice in identifying outputs for given inputs and determining the rules used. Student page 55 offers opportunities to identify two-step functions and to determine equivalent one- and two-step rules.

Assessment

It was possible to assess students' understanding of simple functions during the introductory discussion. As students found outputs and identified rules for two-step functions, it was possible to evaluate their ability to extend their thinking to more complex situations and to assess their proficiency with calculations. Completed student pages provide additional indicators of those concepts students understand and those that may need further attention.

NCTM Standards Summary

Representing functions in flowcharts and in table form served as visual aids to students as they searched for patterns that would reveal function rules. Reasoning was important as students identified patterns, formulated rules for one- and two-step functions. Students used reasoning as they created functions of their own. Explaining their strategies and justifying their choice of rules provided students the opportunity to communicate their thinking and clarify their understanding of functions.

Answers

Page 54

1. 12, 36
2. 5, 14
3. 7, 19
4. 30, 5
5. 18, 24, 30, 48, 66
6. 0, 4, 6, 10, 18
7. 0, 30, 70, 120, 180
8. 3, 4, 5, 7, 11

Page 55

1. C
2. B
3. D
4. 54, 68; Answers may vary. Multiply by 7; add 5.
5. 6, 42; Answers may vary. Subtract 3; multiply by 3.

Name

Using Two-Step Functions

Complete each flowchart.

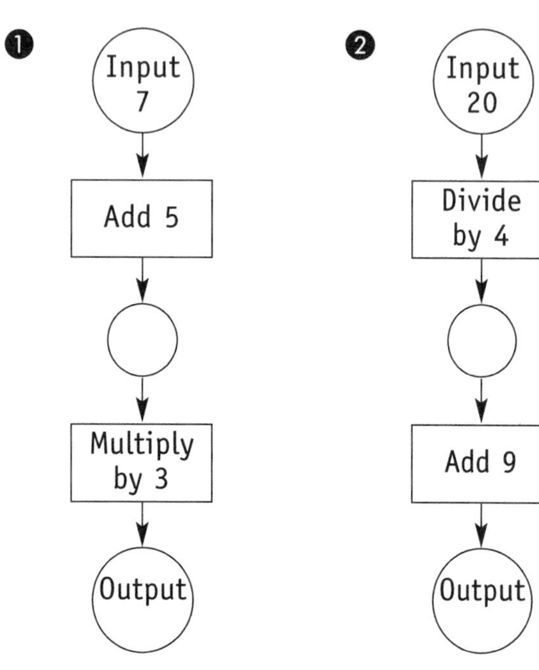

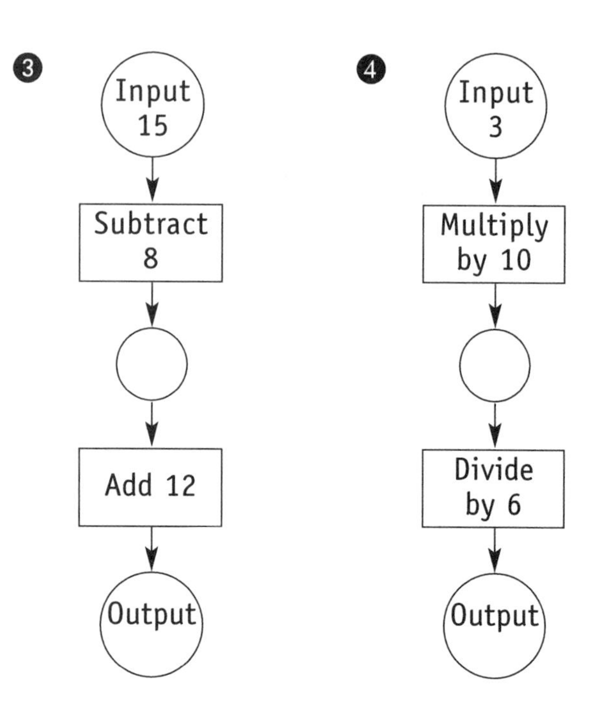

Complete each table.

5. Rule: Add 3; multiply by 6.

Input	Output
0	
1	
2	
5	
8	

6. Rule: Multiply by 4; divide by 2.

Input	Output
0	
2	
3	
5	
9	

7. Rule: Subtract 5; multiply by 10.

Input	Output
5	
8	
12	
17	
23	

8. Rule: Add 8; divide by 3.

Input	Output
1	
4	
7	
13	
25	

Name ______________________________

Using Two-Step Functions

Circle the letter of the best choice.

1. When 5 is the input, the output is 14. Which of the following could be the rule?

   a. Multiply by 2; add 2.
   b. Add 3; multiply by 2.
   c. Add 2; multiply by 2.
   d. Subtract 1; multiply by 3.

2. When 6 is the input, the output is 2. Which of the following could be the rule?

   a. Add 4; divide by 2.
   b. Multiply by 2; divide by 6.
   c. Subtract 4; multiply by 2.
   d. Divide by 2; add 1.

3. When 8 is the input, the output is 20. Which of the following could NOT be the rule?

   a. Multiply by 3; subtract 4.
   b. Add 2; multiply by 2.
   c. Subtract 3; multiply by 4.
   d. Divide by 4; multiply by 5.

Write a two-step rule that works for each input/output table. Use your rules to find the missing outputs.

4.

Input	Output
0	5
1	12
2	19
5	40
7	
9	

Rule: ______________________________

5.

Input	Output
5	
6	9
10	21
14	33
17	
20	51

Rule: ______________________________

Exploring Ordered Pairs

Introduction

Objective → Students will be able to graph ordered pairs and identify patterns.

Context → Students have worked with numerical patterns. They have used grids to interpret graphs and have been introduced to graphing on the coordinate plane. This lesson develops concepts that will prepare students for graphing linear equations in the future.

NCTM Standards Focus

In this standards-based lesson, students will identify patterns in sets of ordered pairs and their visual representations on the coordinate plane. Working from ordered pairs to graph and from graph to ordered pairs, students will extend patterns they identify. This approach will strengthen students' understanding of coordinate graphing and prepare them for graphing linear relations.

Representation Students will compare visual and symbolic representations of the same information as they draw points on a coordinate plane that represent ordered pairs and write ordered pairs that represent points on the plane.

Reasoning and Proof Students will use reasoning to identify patterns formed by sets of ordered pairs and also by sets of points drawn on a coordinate plane. They will predict additional ordered pairs or points that fit the patterns identified and will verify their predictions. Students will make generalizations about patterns they find and will create their own patterns.

Communication Students will explain, both orally and in writing, the common features they observe as they graph sets of ordered pairs.

Teaching Plan

Materials → Student pages 60–61; grid transparency; grid paper

Begin the lesson by reviewing how to locate a point on the coordinate plane. Display a transparency of a grid with the point (2, 3) marked, and go over the steps for determining and recording the coordinates that identify the point. Emphasize that the two coordinates are called an *ordered pair* because their order is important in identifying the point. Demonstrate how the point named by (3, 2) is different than the point named by (2, 3).

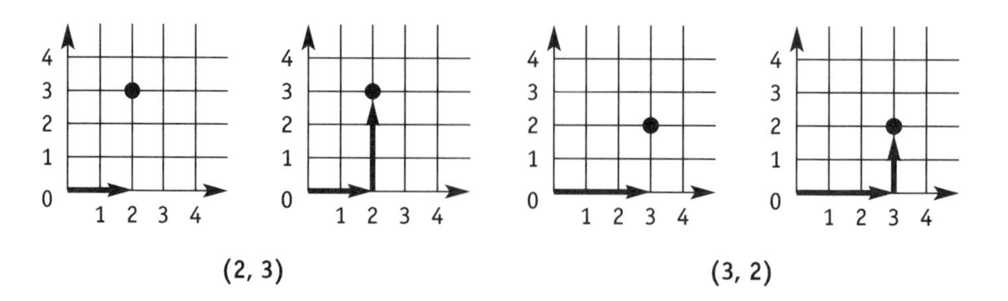

Distribute student page 60. Tell students they will be looking for patterns in sets of ordered pairs. For each activity, present the given set of ordered pairs. Instruct students to graph each set on their worksheets. Have students work individually or in pairs to complete the activities.

Activity 1

Ask students to graph the points (1, 1), (2, 2), and (3, 3).

Name another ordered pair that fits the same pattern. Describe the pattern. [(4, 4), (5, 5) and so on. The x- and y-coordinates are both the same number.] *Just by looking at your grid, could you find another point whose ordered pair has two numbers that are the same? Explain your thinking.* (Students may suggest that the points seem to be along a diagonal line on the grid, or they may observe that each succeeding point is 1 up and 1 right from the previous point.) *Find the coordinates that identify your point. Was your prediction correct?*

Activity 2

Ask students to graph the points (1, 0), (3, 0), and (5, 0).

What do you notice about this set of ordered pairs? (The second number, or y-coordinate, in each ordered pair is 0.) *Describe the graph of this set of points.* (All of the points lie on the horizontal axis.) Ask students to predict another ordered pair that will fit this pattern and to graph that ordered pair to see if their predictions are correct.

Activity 3

Dictate the ordered pairs (0, 2), (0, 3), (0, 4).

What do you notice about this new set of ordered pairs? (The first number, or x-coordinate, in each pair is 0.) *Can you predict what the graph of these ordered pairs will look like? Explain your thinking.* (Students may reason that since all the points $(x, 0)$ were on the horizontal axis, that all the points $(0, y)$ will lie on the vertical axis.) Then have students graph the points to see if their predictions are correct. Have them write another ordered pair that fits the pattern and graph the point for that ordered pair.

Activity 4

Have students study the set of ordered pairs (1, 5), (2, 5), and (4, 5).

What do you notice about this set of ordered pairs? (In each of the ordered pairs the second number, or y-coordinate, is 5.) *What information does the second number, or y-coordinate, tell you?* (The number of spaces to move up) *Can you predict what this set of ordered pairs will look like after they have been graphed?* (Students may suggest that all of the points will lie on the horizontal line corresponding to 5.) Instruct students to check their prediction(s) by graphing. Then, tell them to draw another point on their graph that fits the same pattern. *What is the second number in the ordered pair of the point you drew?* (5)

NOW CHALLENGE STUDENTS to write a set of three ordered pairs which, when graphed, will lie on the line that is 2 units to the right of the y-axis. *Which number will be the same in each of the ordered pairs? Explain your thinking.* [The first number, or x-coordinate; all of the points are the same number of spaces to the right, in this case 2. A possible set of points is (2, 0), (2, 1), and (2, 2).] Tell students to check the coordinates they identify by graphing the three ordered pairs they chose.

What Might Happen . . . What to Do

Students may have difficulty naming the coordinates for three different points that are 2 units to the right of the *y*-axis. Tell students to draw three points on their grid, and to make each 2 units to the right of the *y*-axis.

Have them identify the ordered pair for each point and then explain the pattern. They can then write a different set of ordered pairs for points on the line that would be 3 units to the right of the *y*-axis.

Conclude the lesson by inviting students to create their own sets of ordered pairs that produce a pattern. For example, they may use pairs where each second number is one greater than the first number or each second number is three times the first number. You may wish to provide students with extra sheets of grid paper so they can explore the visual representations and strengthen their understanding about the relationship between the numbers in ordered pairs. Have students share, compare, and discuss their work.

Extension

Have students draw capital letters such as E, F, H, I, L, or T on grid paper and then identify the ordered pairs for points on their letters. Encourage students to describe any patterns they observe in the ordered pairs.

Student Pages

Student page 60 provides recording space for lesson Activities 1–4. Student page 61 includes exercises to reinforce students' proficiency in identifying and graphing ordered pairs. There are also exercises for exploring patterns visually and analytically.

Assessment

As students completed the lesson activities, you were able to assess their skill in identifying and graphing ordered pairs. It was possible to evaluate students' understanding of patterns created by sets of ordered pairs as they described and extended patterns on the grid. Their answers to the practice exercises allowed you to determine students' fluency with the fundamental concepts of the lesson.

NCTM Standards Summary

Students represented points as ordered pairs and represented ordered pairs as points on a grid. They examined ordered pairs to find patterns and explained how these patterns were represented visually. Students predicted other ordered pairs that would fit each pattern and verified their predictions by graphing. Students reasoned and made generalizations about the graphs they produced and were challenged to create their own patterns. The exploratory approach of the lesson enabled students to move beyond rote identifying and graphing of ordered pairs to considering relationships between the numbers in the ordered pair and the type of graph that resulted. Throughout the lesson, students shared their insights both orally and in writing.

Answers

Page 60

Activity 1 (1, 1), (2, 2), (3, 3)
Activity 2 (1, 0), (3, 0), (5, 0)
Activity 3 (0, 2), (0, 3), (0,4)
Activity 4 (1, 5), (2, 5), (4, 5)
In each of the activities, points on the graphs should match the ordered pairs.

Page 61

1. *B*
2. *F*
3. *H*
4. *J*
5. (10, 11)
6. (9, 0)
7. (13, 1)
8. (4, 11)
9. *M* and *G*
10. The second number is 2 more than the first.
11. Points should be properly placed on the grid.
12 Answers will vary.
13. *D* = (3, 4) does not fit. Students' graphs should show all points except *D*. When corrected to fit, *D* = (3, 7). Students may explain that starting at A, each point is another space to the right and up two; they may visualize the straight line on which the points lie, or they may observe that the second number is one more than twice the first.

Name ______________________________

Exploring Ordered Pairs

Graph the set of ordered pairs for each activity.

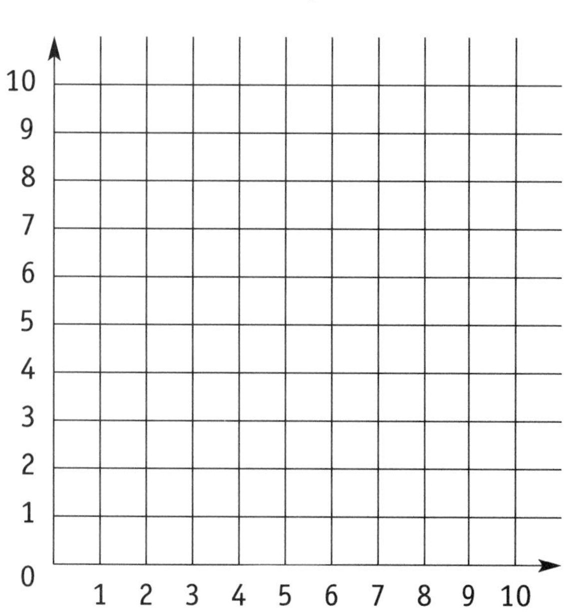

Activity 2

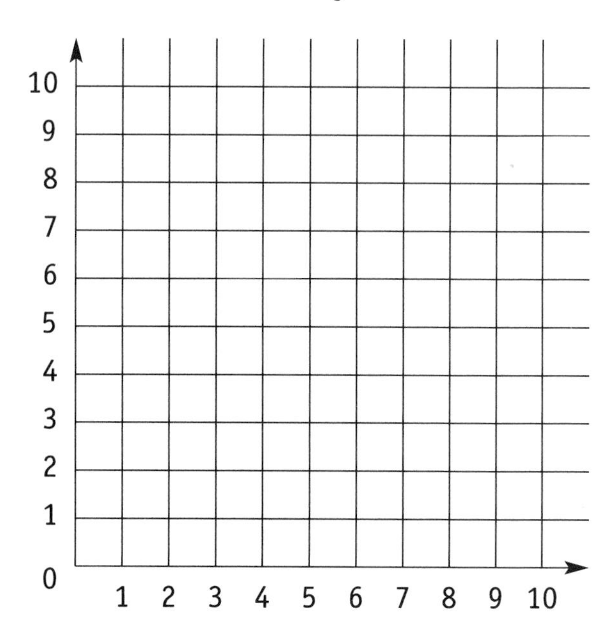

Activity 3

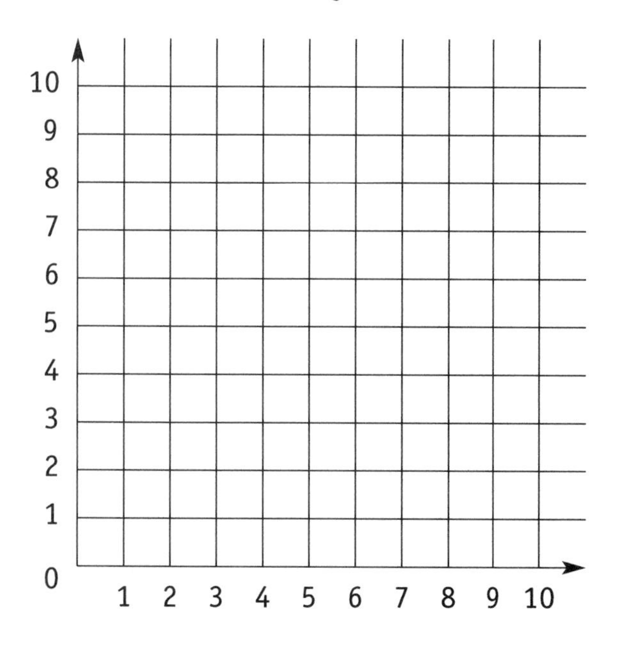

Activity 4

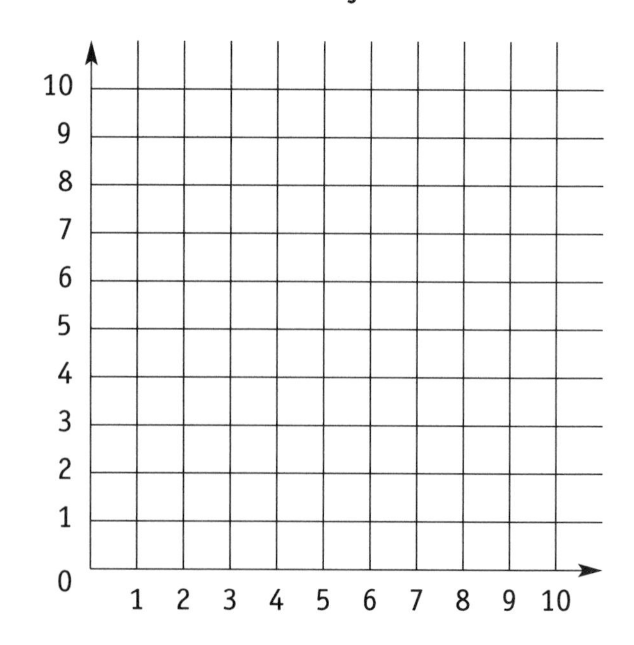

Name

Exploring Ordered Pairs

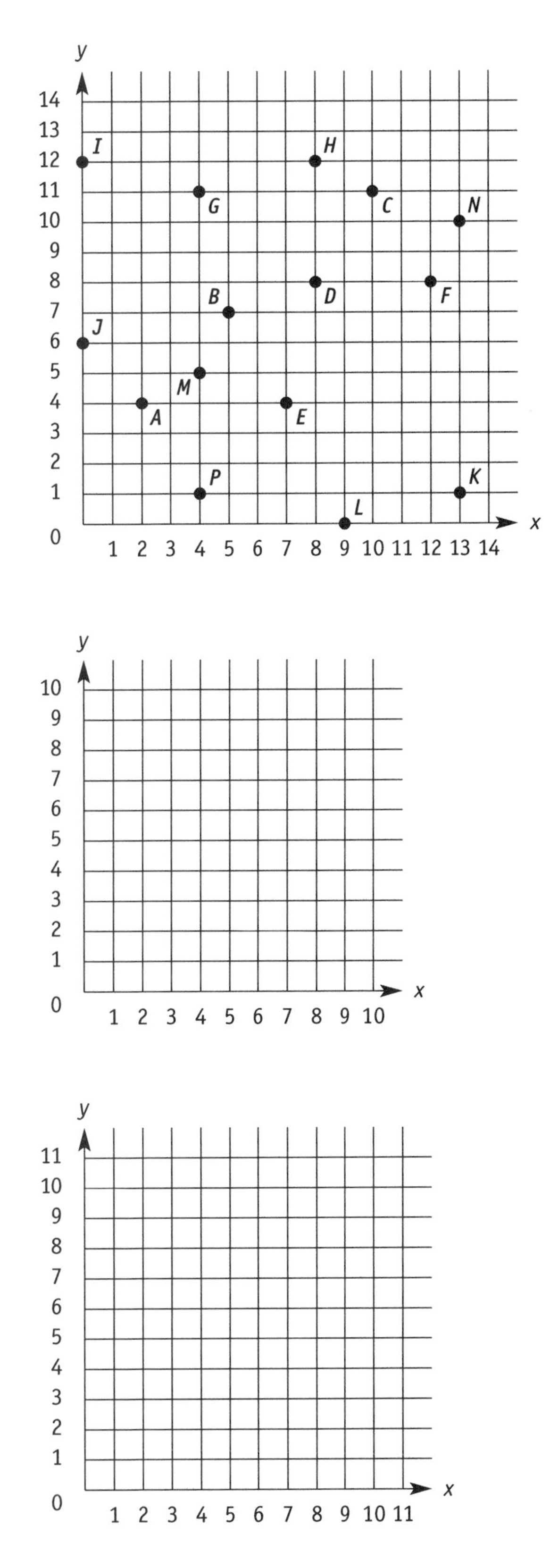

Write the letter for each ordered pair.

1. (5, 7)
2. (12, 8)
3. (8, 12)
4. (0, 6)

Write the ordered pair for each letter or description.

5. *C*
6. *L*
7. *K*
8. *G*
9. A point with the same *x*-coordinate as *P*

Use the ordered pairs (1, 3), (4, 6), (0, 2), (5, 7).

10. Describe the pattern.
11. Graph the points.
12. Write four additional ordered pairs that fit the pattern. Graph them.
13. **Challenge** All but one of the points described below fit a pattern. Graph these points. Write the ordered pair that does not fit the pattern and explain why it does not fit the pattern. Then rewrite the ordered pair, changing it to fit the pattern.

$A = (0, 1)$ $B = (1, 3)$

$C = (2, 5)$ $D = (3, 4)$

$E = (4, 9)$ $F = (5, 11)$

Discovering the Properties of Multiplication

Introduction

Objective → Students will understand and recognize the Commutative Property, Associative Property, Property of One, and the Zero Property for multiplication.

Context → Students are already familiar with the multiplication of whole numbers. This lesson comes near the end of a unit on multiplication.

Discovering the Properties of Multiplication

Learn

Properties of multiplication help you to find products.
Numbers that are multiplied together to give a product are called factors.

$8 \times 3 = 24$

8 and 3 are factors. 24 is the product of multiplying the factors 8 and 3.

Commutative Property

The order in which factors are multiplied does not change the product.

$4 \times 2 = 8$ $\quad 2 \times 4 = 8$

Associative Property

When there are more than 2 factors, the order in which they are grouped does not change the product.

$(2 \times 2) \times 3 = 12$ $\quad 2 \times (2 \times 3) = 12$

$4 \times 3 = 12$ $\quad 2 \times 6 = 12$

Property of One

Any number multiplied by 1 has that number for a product.

$7 \times 1 = 7$

Zero Property

Any number multiplied by 0 has a product of 0.

$5 \times 0 = 0$

NCTM Process Standards Analysis and Focus

The standards analysis examines how the process standards have been incorporated into the above lesson. By increasing the focus on three of the process standards, a more effective and meaningful lesson can be presented. The suggestions offered can help you to think about how this might be accomplished.

Reasoning and Proof A discussion question asks students to explain their thinking and give examples of properties for addition and multiplication that are similar.

Suggestion → **Have students conduct a series of investigations through which they will develop and generalize the properties of multiplication. Encourage students to search for counter-examples so they become aware of methods used to test ideas.**

Discuss

Which multiplication properties are like the addition properties? Which are different. Explain your answers and give examples.

Try

Use the four Properties of Multiplication to solve.

1. 1×74 **2.** 0×6 **3.** 1×343 **4.** $1 \times 9{,}934$ **5.** 0×43

6. $4 \times 3 = 3 \times \_$ **7.** $8 \times \_ = 5 \times 8$ **8.** $(3 \times 4) \times 6 = 3 \times (\_ \times 6)$

Practice

Find the missing number. Tell what Property of Multiplication helped you find the number.

9. $1 \times \_ = 7$ **10.** $\_ \times 12 = 0$ **11.** $4 \times 3 = \_ \times 4$

12. $8 \times (\_ \times 3) = (8 \times 2) \times 3$ **13.** $\_ \times 5 = 5 \times 6$

14. $9 \times \_ = 0$ **15.** $(2 \times 3) \times 7 = 2 \times (3 \times \_)$

16. $(12 \times \_) \times \_ = 12$ **17.** $0 \times \_ = 0$

18. The product of two factors is 0. Can you name one of the factors? What could the other factor be? Explain.

19. The product of two numbers is 19. What do you think those two numbers are?

Review

Add or subtract.

20. $352 - 26$ **21.** $505 + 621$ **22.** $4{,}576 - 2{,}631$ **23.** $5{,}005 + 2{,}116$

Communication The lesson asks students to explain the properties in their own words.

Suggestion → **Provide opportunities for students to discuss their ideas and generalize rules. Increasing communication will help clarify and reinforce the concepts being developed.**

Representation The lesson illustrates the properties of multiplication with a diagram and with numbers.

Suggestion → **Instruct students to write and illustrate their generalizations. This task involves representation at several levels: using numbers, words, and diagrams.**

Problem Solving The lesson includes questions that require reasoning; however, actual problem-solving opportunities are not included.

Connections The lesson asks students to make connections between the properties of multiplication and addition.

The teaching plan that follows shows how the suggestions for increasing the focus on the process standards can be implemented.

Revised Teaching Plan

WRITE THE INVESTIGATION PLAN and investigation questions on the board for students to refer to during the lesson. Explain to students that they will use the investigation plan and questions as a guide while they work to make some important discoveries about multiplication. Organize students into groups of three or four. Have each group select a scribe to take notes about the group's observations.

Investigation Plan

1. Pick 3 different whole numbers.
2. Use 2 numbers at a time. Multiply in as many different orders as you can.
3. Use all 3 numbers. Multiply in as many different orders as you can.
4. Try multiplying each number by 1.
5. Try multiplying each number by 0.
6. Stop after each step and discuss what you notice.

Investigation Questions

1. Does the order in which you multiply two factors matter?
2. If you are multiplying three or more factors together, does the order matter?
3. Is there a single number that when multiplied by any factor gives you that factor as a product?
4. Is there a single number that when multiplied by any factor gives zero as its product?

Review the terms *factor* and *product* with the class, and encourage students to use these terms as they discuss and share ideas. Tell students that each group will be responsible for finding all answers and presenting as much information as they can to prove that their answers are correct. Instruct them to consider the questions as they work through the steps, and encourage them to prepare illustrations that present their generalizations.

Model working through each step of the investigation plan with students. Allow a few minutes for students to explore each step. For step 1, write the numbers 8, 5, and 2 on the board. Introduce step 2 by picking two of the numbers and asking students to help you write all of the multiplication problems that can be created. (There are two.) Then pick another pair and do the same, and repeat the process for the third pair. Explain that the goal is to look for patterns in the way multiplication works. Remind students to discuss any observations or thoughts that they have so far and to begin formulating their answer to the first investigation question.

What Might Happen . . . What to Do

Discovering mathematical principles on their own may be unfamiliar to some students, and you may see them waiting passively for the "rule" so that they can do it "right." This is a big challenge to any discovery-based teaching! Here are a few approaches to consider. (1) Talk about the fact that the math we learn in school had to be discovered by people who worked hard at looking for patterns and underlying principles. (2) Support and reward independent thinking and new ideas students share in class even when they are not completely in line with conventional understanding. (3) Offer more opportunities for problem solving, especially with problems that are new or different from what students have already seen.

Next, direct students' attention to step 3 of the investigation plan and have them use all three numbers, multiplying them in as many different orders as they can. (There are six.) Ask students to think about the second investigation question and again discuss and write down their observations.

Move around the room looking for opportunities to engage and support students in becoming actively involved in this investigation. You may notice some students having trouble keeping track of the different sets of problems they are investigating. Encourage students to choose one number and use it as the first factor in as many sentences as possible. Monitor students as they work to make sure that understanding the process of this investigation is not a stumbling block—discovering the underlying properties of multiplication is the ultimate goal.

Have groups communicate their thinking after checking each set of numbers and record their ideas as they complete each step of the investigation plan. This will help them clarify their thinking and see their work as a logical step-by-step process in which one discovery or idea can be checked against new evidence. As you interact with groups, look for ways to model this process. *At first you noticed that 8 × 5 has the same result as 5 × 8. Did the idea that order doesn't matter when you multiply two numbers together hold up as you tried other combinations? Do you think order will matter more now that you're multiplying three numbers together?*

f.y.i.

You may want to have each group rotate their scribe before they begin step 4. Consider assigning a reluctant student in a group to take on this role. Being the "scribe" can be strong incentive for paying attention and staying involved.

INSTRUCT STUDENTS TO READ STEP 4 of the investigation plan. Students should choose one of the three numbers and multiply it by 1, and then repeat the procedure with each of the other two numbers. Have students read the third investigation question. Remind them to write down their thoughts and observations and draft their answers.

Call students' attention to step 5 of the investigation plan. Make sure that students understand that they are to multiply each of the three numbers by 0 and record the results. Ask students to read the fourth investigation question and to again discuss and write down their thoughts and observations.

Break up student groups and have students repeat steps 2–5 the investigation individually using the numbers 7, 6, and 4. Before students begin, you may want to be specific about the level of writing you expect after each step, since well-organized notes support the reasoning process going on in students' minds.

Allow time for students to work on their own, and then bring groups back together to have students compare their answers and their thoughts and observations. This additional communication will help students clarify and refine their ideas.

FINALLY, WRITE 3, 5, AND 6 ON THE BOARD, and ask students to predict what will happen within each of the four investigation steps. This will help students move toward the goal of generalizing their ideas into mathematical principles. Have groups verify their predictions by computing the answers.

Complete the investigation by leading students to summarize the rules they discovered. Refer them back to the investigation questions, and encourage them to formulate an answer and create an illustration for each question. Record their rules on the board next to the questions or on chart paper.

CLOSE THE LESSON BY CHALLENGING students to test the validity of the principles they've discovered with a search for counter-examples to incorporate more reasoning and proof into the lesson. *Are there any numbers for which your conclusions will not be true?* Students should be aware that just because they've found several cases where the factors can be reversed without changing the product doesn't that mean it works for all numbers. *How many cases do you think would be needed to prove something? 1? 10? 100 or more?* You might discuss that some ideas have been tested thousands of times by many people before being offered as true.

Student Pages

Students should now be ready to complete exercises similar to those on the reduced student pages. Consider having students complete the exercises and label each with the corresponding multiplication property.

Assessment

In this discovery-based lesson that engaged students in reasoning and communicating about their discoveries, there was ample opportunity to assess students' understanding of the four multiplication properties. By observing students work independently and in groups there were chances to monitor their thinking and evaluate how they expressed their ideas orally and in writing. These activities also provided opportunities to observe their ability to examine new evidence to refine and clarify their thinking.

NCTM Standards Summary

Students used reasoning as they collected evidence in a series of investigations and drew conclusions that they generalized into mathematical principles. Rather than simply learning facts, students developed understanding through active reasoning. Communication supported this process at each step as students worked together in groups discussing ideas and recording their findings. Representation was a key component of the lesson as students employed words, numbers, and diagrams to express ideas.

Standard 3 **Geometry**

AT THE FOURTH GRADE LEVEL, geometry includes a lot of work with two- and three-dimensional shapes, the coordinate system, and transformations. Our lessons are derived from these important topics. They include a lesson on classifying quadrilaterals, a lesson on understanding the coordinate system, a lesson in which students draw views of three-dimensional shapes, and a lesson on exploring rotations.

Three lessons model how the process standards can be used to teach content. A fourth lesson is a hypothetical textbook lesson that we have revised to be more standards based. These four lessons do not represent the entire curriculum, but rather provide glimpses of how, with a more concentrated effort to incorporate the process standards, better mathematics teaching and learning can be achieved.

In one lesson we have chosen, students identify and classify the different quadrilaterals. By approaching this lesson from a reasoning-and-proof angle, students have to decide whether to agree or disagree with statements about the quadrilaterals. The process standards of representation and communication are also important, as students express their thoughts both verbally and in writing.

Another lesson we have chosen provides a foundation for students to understand the coordinate system. Through problem solving, representation, and communication, students develop a system in which they can describe a location for any object in the classroom.

A third lesson we have chosen asks students to build a three-dimensional shape from two-dimensional drawings. Students use their visual reasoning skills to determine how to build their three-dimensional shapes. Connections are made to future career choices, as artists and architects both utilize these skills in their respective jobs.

The hypothetical textbook lesson we have chosen to revise explores rotations. Through better incorporation of the process standards of representation, reasoning and proof, and communication, students will develop a more in-depth understanding of rotations. They will identify when a new orientation of a figure is a rotation and when it is not.

Standard 3 Lessons

- **Classifying Quadrilaterals**
- **Understanding the Coordinate System**
- **Drawing Views of Three-Dimensional Shapes**
- **Exploring Rotations**

Classifying Quadrilaterals

Introduction

Objective → Students will be able to identify trapezoids, parallelograms, rhombi, rectangles, and squares.

Context → Students have had previous experiences with two-dimensional shapes. They will go on to learn more about the properties of the shapes.

NCTM Standards Focus

The introduction of different types of quadrilaterals and their corresponding characteristics or properties lays the foundation for students' subsequent studies in geometry. In this standards-based lesson, students build their knowledge and understanding from the ground up. They make drawings of quadrilaterals and use these to learn and understand the different properties of the various types of quadrilaterals.

Reasoning and Proof Students apply their knowledge of the various characteristics or properties of different types of quadrilaterals. They use their drawings of figures to determine whether they agree or disagree with statements made about these quadrilaterals.

Communication Students work cooperatively to create different quadrilaterals. They discuss the characteristics of their shapes and determine whether or not they represent a particular type of quadrilateral. They communicate their ideas both orally and in writing.

Representation Students create figures based on general information about these figures. They also use the representations to make generalizations about the figures.

Teaching Plan

Materials → Student pages 74–75; 2-cm grid paper; rulers

BEGIN THE LESSON by asking students if they know what a quadrilateral is. Point out that the prefix *quad-* means "four" and *lateral* means "sides." A quadrilateral is any shape that has four sides. *What are some shapes that you know are quadrilaterals?* (Square, rectangle, parallelogram, kite, diamond, rhombus, trapezoid) Draw a rectangle on the overhead or board. Ask students to list the characteristics of the figure.

What Students Might Say

- There are two pairs of parallel sides.
- The pairs of opposite sides are the same length (congruent).
- All the angles are right angles.

Introduce or reinforce the vocabulary words *parallel, congruent,* and *right.* Define the terms by referring back to the figure, connecting the terms to their representations. This will give students a visual reference to use as they describe their own figures later in the lesson. Since students will be expected to use this vocabulary during the lesson, be sure they are comfortable with these terms before proceeding with the lesson.

f.y.i.

Have students write these terms and their meanings in their math journals or on a 3 × 5 card for easy reference. These may or may not be terms that students are familiar with. They will be needed for the remainder of the lesson.

PASS OUT A SHEET of 2-cm grid paper and a ruler to each student. Have students work in pairs to draw as many different four-sided figures as they can. Tell them that it is acceptable to draw any four-sided figure. After students have at least ten figures, tell them to stop. Have them select ten different figures and number them 1–10.

Give a copy of student page 74 to each student. Explain to students that they are to complete this chart, using the 10 figures they've selected. You may want to demonstrate how to complete one entry using your figure or a figure from one of the student pairs.

What Might Happen . . . What to Do

Some students may be concerned that there are no columns for zero parallel lines, right angles, or congruent sides. Make sure they understand that if there are no check marks for a figure, there are no parallel lines, right angles, or congruent sides. You may also want to go over the section on the congruent sides. The first column means there is one pair of congruent sides, the second means there are two different pairs of congruent sides and the third means all sides are congruent.

When students have finished, bring them together as a class to discuss their findings. Ask if someone has a figure for which columns A and E are checked. If more than one student has the same columns checked, have the class look at the differences and the similarities in the figures. Looking at different figures with similar attributes will help students clarify their understanding of the attributes. As students talk about their shapes, encourage them to name the shapes (square, rectangle, etc.). Continue the discussion, letting students show their figures and describe the figures' attributes until you think students have a good understanding of the characteristics of quadrilaterals.

f.y.i.

As the discussion continues, encourage students to note that despite variations of other attributes, quadrilaterals always have 4 sides.

Now have students complete the bottom of page 74. You may wish to begin with a class discussion in which students tell what they know about each figure and reach a class description of the attributes or characteristics of the figures. Encourage students to include attributes of both sides and angles for each figure. See the *Answers* section of the lesson for a suggested list of attributes.

f.y.i.

Point out to students that in #5 on student page 75, the word *rhombi* is the plural form of *rhombus.*

Once students have recorded the characteristics of the five types of quadrilaterals, have them look back at their 10 figures. *Do you have any figures of these types? Which ones? Do any of your figures meet the characteristics for more than one type? Which figures and which types?* Engage students in a discussion about their figures. Challenge them to explain how one figure can fit into more than one category of quadrilaterals.

Close the lesson by telling students they will be using what they have learned to make some general statements about these types of figures.

Depending on the amount of time you have, you may either have students do page 75 in class or later. Tell students they should refer to the figures they drew and analyzed earlier in the lesson.

Student Pages

Student page 74 provides a chart with various characteristics for students to check off as they pertain to the quadrilaterals they drew. The page also provides space to describe the characteristics of various quadrilaterals. Student page 75 gives students opportunities to make generalizations about quadrilaterals.

Assessment

You had an opportunity to observe students' understanding as they analyzed their figures and discussed how their figures fit into the charts. Page 75 gave an opportunity to assess students' overall understanding of the figures.

NCTM Standards Summary

Students created multiple representations of quadrilaterals and explored their characteristics, noting characteristics that different quadrilaterals shared. Students used their observations to list the characteristics of various types of quadrilaterals. Finally, they made generalizations about the figures. They communicated their reasoning orally in small group and whole class discussions, as well as in writing.

Answers

Page 74

1. Answers may vary.

2–6. Answers may vary, but should include the following characteristics:
Square: 4 sides of equal length; 4 right angles;
Rectangle: opposite sides are parallel and of equal length; 4 right angles;
Parallelogram: opposite sides are parallel and of equal length;
Rhombus: opposite sides are parallel; all sides are of equal length;
Trapezoid: one pair of parallel sides.

Page 75

1. Disagree; Rectangles have opposite sides of equal length, while squares must have *all* sides of equal length.
2. Agree; A square meets the definition of a rhombus, but a rhombus does not need to have four right angles.
3. Disagree; A trapezoid needs only one pair of parallel sides. It is possible for a trapezoid to have four different angles.
4. Disagree; A quadrilateral needs only four sides and four angles.
5. Agree; All rhombi have pairs of opposite sides that are parallel and of equal length.

Name ______________________

Classifying Quadrilaterals

❶ Place a check mark in each column that applies to the figures you've drawn.

	A	B	C	D	E	F	G
Figure	1 pair of parallel sides	2 pairs of parallel sides	2 right angles	4 right angles	1 pair of congruent sides	2 pairs of congruent sides	4 congruent sides
1							
2							
3							
4							
5							
6							
7							
8							
9							
10							

Describe the characteristics of each shape.

❷ Square ______________________

❸ Rectangle ______________________

❹ Parallelogram ______________________

❺ Rhombus ______________________

❻ Trapezoid ______________________

Name ____________________

Classifying Quadrilaterals

For each statement, circle *Agree* or *Disagree*. Explain your reasoning.

1. All rectangles are squares. Agree Disagree

____

____

____

2. All squares are rhombi, but not all rhombi are squares. Agree Disagree

____

____

____

3. All trapezoids have two pairs of congruent angles. Agree Disagree

____

____

____

4. All quadrilaterals have at least one pair of parallel sides. Agree Disagree

____

____

____

5. All rhombi are parallelograms. Agree Disagree

____

____

____

© Creative Publications Permission is given by the publisher to reproduce this page for classroom or home use only.

Understanding the Coordinate System

Introduction

Objective → Students will be able to describe position in relation to a reference point.

Context → This is an introductory lesson to the coordinate system. After this lesson students will begin to graph some simple linear equations.

NCTM Standards Focus

This introduction of the coordinate system lays the foundation for students' later work in algebra and geometry. In this standards-based lesson, students will be actively engaged in a problem-solving situation where they see a purpose for having a system to identify and communicate the location of a given object.

Problem Solving Students work to devise an effective method for determining the location of a particular object in the classroom. Students are then presented with a hypothetical situation where they need to be able to communicate the location of any object in the classroom.

Representation Students use several forms of representation to work with the concept of the coordinate system. Later they work with the first quadrant of the system and represent information in that quadrant.

Communication Students work collectively and collaboratively to devise a system for locating a designated object in the classroom. They communicate their methods with one another and discuss the effectiveness and accuracy of the methods used. They connect this concept of communication to the coordinate system.

Teaching Plan

Materials → Student pages 80–81; transparency of student page 81

EXPLAIN TO STUDENTS that in today's lesson, they will be challenged to devise a system that can be used to describe the precise location of any object in the classroom. Spend a few minutes discussing with students why such a system might be useful—for example, in a search-and-rescue mission.

Put students in groups and assign each group an object in the room. Tell students that their goal is to write a set of directions that tells other students how to find the object. In doing so they should think about devising a system that can be used not just to find their object, but to find any object. They should devise a system that can also be used by others to locate any object in the room.

© Creative Publications

Circulate around the room as groups work on their systems. Make sure that students can put their directions in writing. One question that may help them think of developing a system as opposed to just getting directions to finding the one item one time is, *Will your directions be useful for someone unfamiliar with this classroom?*

f.y.i.

In choosing objects for students to find it is probably best to choose objects that are large and out in the open such as someone's desk. Also, at this point it is probably best not to choose a very large object such as a long bookcase. However, once a system for locating items is established, it would be good to talk about how to describe the location of a large object.

WHEN STUDENTS ARE FINISHED bring them back together and have them try each other's directions. Have groups try each other's directions one set of directions at a time, so they can learn from what each group has done. This is an excellent time to focus on students' communication. Often as students watch another group try to follow their directions, they see where the directions were unclear. Take this opportunity to work on precise language. Let the students trying to find the object follow the directions as they are written and then, if needed, let the group that wrote the directions revise them with help from the class.

After each group's directions have been tested and revised, involve students in a discussion about the pros and cons of the different ideas. Students are likely to have come up with two general types of systems.

- A relational system that describes the location of an object in terms of other objects (To the left of the teacher's desk, in front of the window, etc.).
- A grid system similar to what might be used on a map.

While each type might work well for the exercise students have just completed, the relational system will be difficult to use in other situations because it does not allow for a standard configuration. Students will see this as they go to the next exercise.

NOW SKETCH THE OUTLINE of a blank piece of paper on chart paper or on the overhead projector. Put an X somewhere on the paper. Tell students to think of the systems that they just made and see if they can use them or devise new ones to tell others how to mark the same location on their papers.

Allow students time to discuss how the methods they used in the previous activity apply to the current task. As they do ask them about the differences between the previous activity and this one. An important difference is that,

© Creative Publications

in this activity, there are no objects other than the X. In this case, a relational system will not be useful. Depending on the time available, you may or may not wish to pursue this line of thinking with the class.

Tell students that there is a system called the *coordinate system* that is used in mathematics to identify the location of points or objects. Show the class a transparency of student page 81. Ask them to analyze the system and explain how it is similar to or different from what they devised during the class so far.

Point to one of the letters on the graph. Ask students how they would describe the location of the point named by the letter. After they respond, take some time to discuss how to use the coordinates of a point to describe its location. Introduce the vocabulary below and explain how to record an ordered pair.

- *x-axis:* the horizontal line at the base of the grid
- *y-axis:* the vertical line that intersects at 0 on the x-axis
- *origin:* the intersection of the x- and y-axes
- *x-coordinate:* distance measured horizontally; the first number in an ordered pair
- *y-coordinate:* distance measured vertically; the second number in an ordered pair
- *ordered pair:* the name of a point recorded as (x, y); for example, (3, 2)

What Might Happen . . . What to Do

Students commonly forget which number to write first in ordered pairs. The following analogy may help. Since the grid looks somewhat like a building, have students think of the coordinate plane as an elevator. You always must move horizontally to enter the elevator before you can move vertically. Thus *x*, the movement along the horizontal axis comes first, then *y*, the movement along the vertical axis.

Spend as much time as you think necessary talking about the coordinate system. If you wish, do student page 80 page with the students.

When students have finished page 80, have them share their responses. Discuss any differences in answers, encouraging students to share their reasoning for arriving at their answer.

© Creative Publications

To close the lesson, review the process for identifying and graphing ordered pairs. Reinforce the formal vocabulary and challenge students to identify other real-world applications for this concept.

For homework, pass out a copy of student page 81. This page will allow students to practice graphing ordered pairs that, when connected, will form geometric figures. It also provides students the opportunity to write ordered pairs that when connected, will form certain geometric figures. You may wish to give students extra copies of the page or extra graph paper so they can graph one figure per page.

Student Pages

Student page 80 provides students with practice identifying and graphing ordered pairs. Student page 81 provides students with additional graphing practice that leads to forming geometric figures.

Assessment

There was opportunity to assess students' understanding as they worked in groups to develop systems to describe the location of a particular object. The follow-up discussion and subsequent work applying their systems to the problem of identifying the location of a single point, provided you with an excellent chance to see the connections students were making. Finally, as students completed student pages 80 and 81, you were able to see how well they used the coordinate system.

NCTM Standards Summary

In this lesson, students used problem solving and communication as they determined an effective system for identifying the location of an object and described their systems so that other groups of students could use the systems. Precision in communication was a focus of the lesson. Students used the representational coordinate grid system to make graphic representations of the location of points.

Answers

Page 80

1. (1, 7)
2. (3, 2)
3. (5, 10)
4. (6, 0)
5. (8, 4)
6. (10, 8)

7–12. Students will plot points and label them.

Page 81

1. Points will form a square.
2. Points will form an outline of a house.
3. Points will form a parallelogram.
4. Points will form a triangle.
5. Student responses will vary.
6. Student responses will vary.

© Creative Publications

Name ______________________

Understanding the Coordinate System

Use the grid.

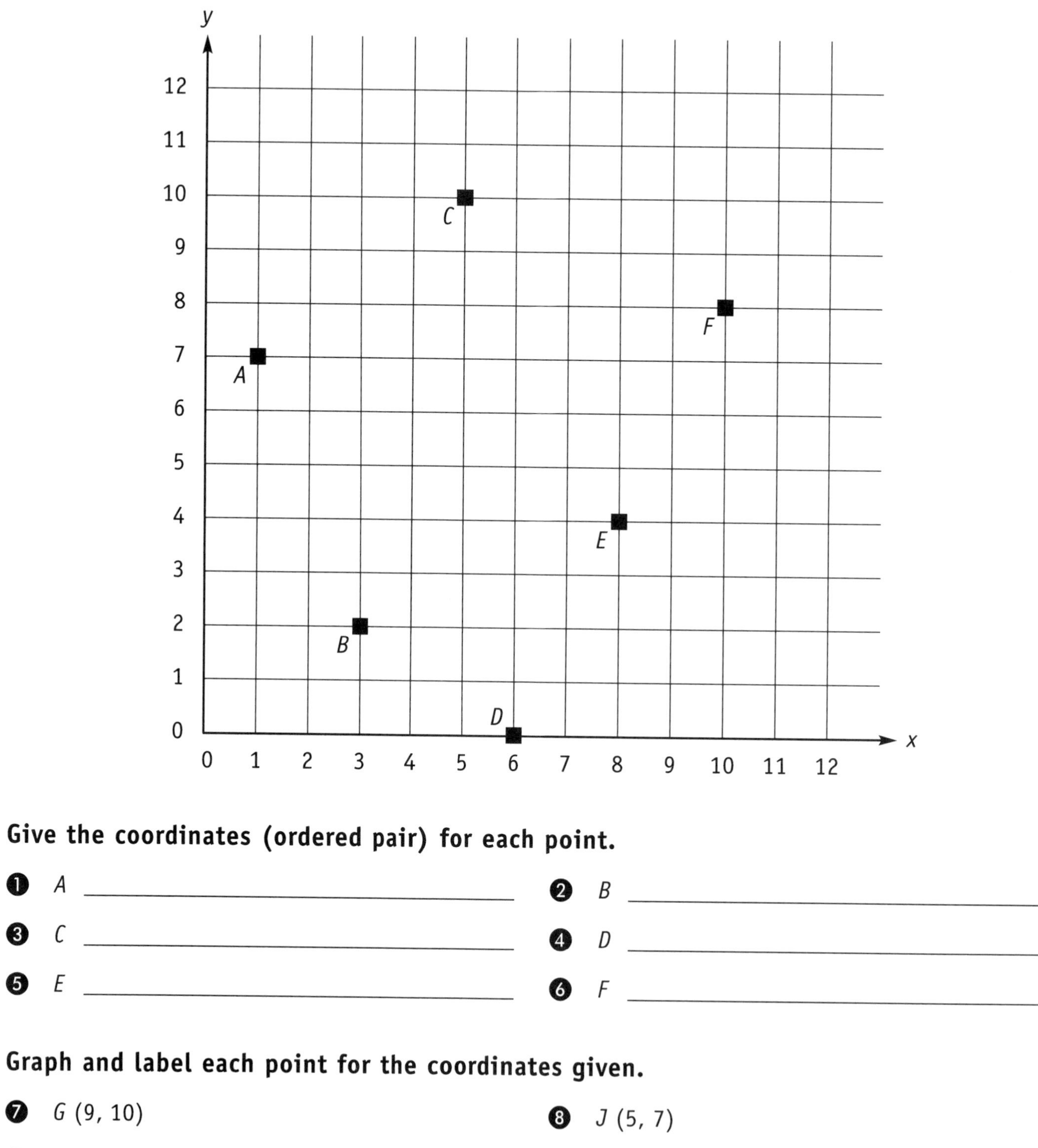

Give the coordinates (ordered pair) for each point.

❶ *A* ______________________ ❷ *B* ______________________

❸ *C* ______________________ ❹ *D* ______________________

❺ *E* ______________________ ❻ *F* ______________________

Graph and label each point for the coordinates given.

❼ *G* (9, 10) ❽ *J* (5, 7)

❾ *H* (2, 5) ❿ *K* (1, 11)

⓫ *I* (12, 3) ⓬ *L* (0, 3)

© Creative Publications. Permission is given by the publisher to reproduce this page for

Name ______________________

Understanding the Coordinate System

Use the grid.

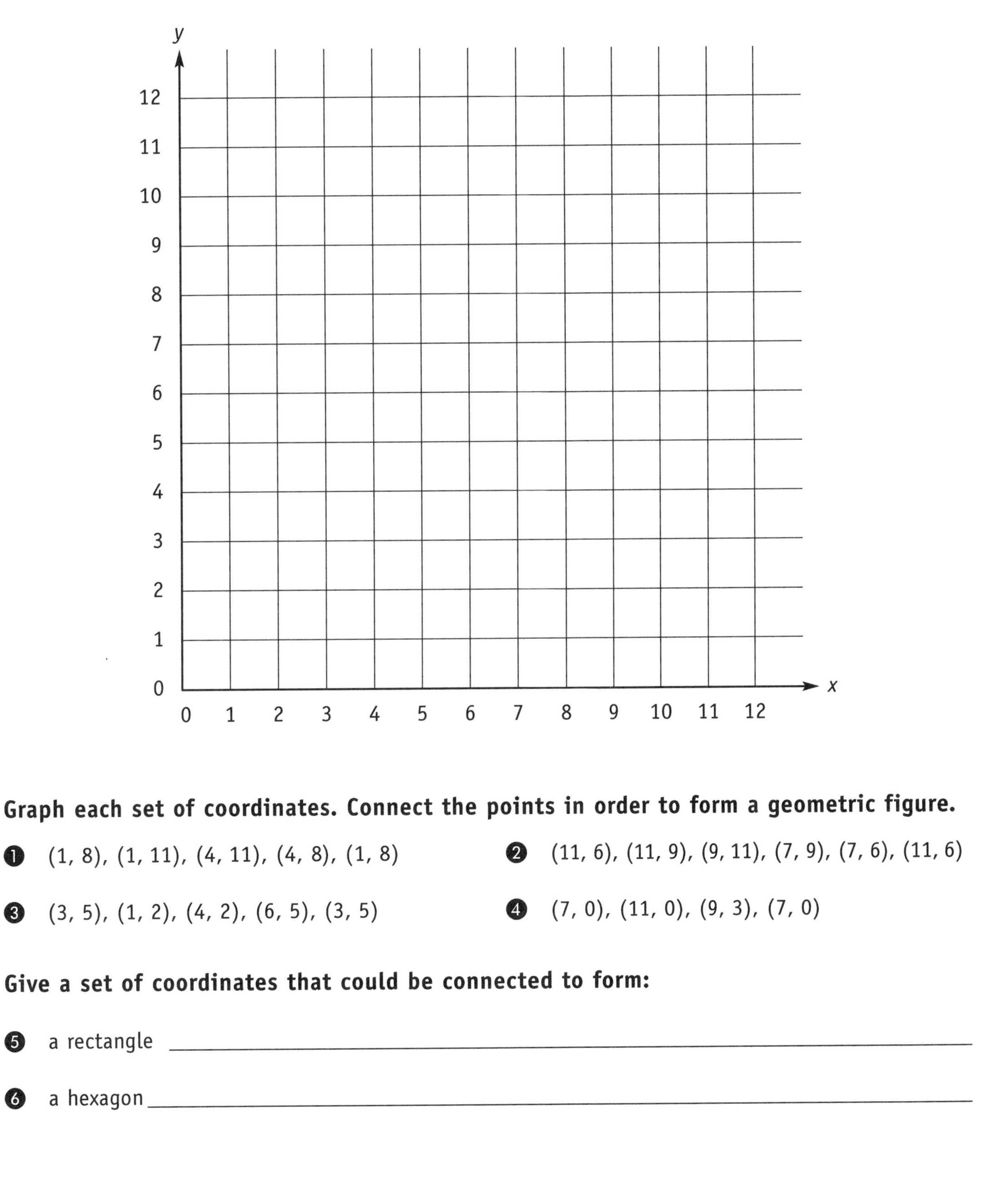

Graph each set of coordinates. Connect the points in order to form a geometric figure.

❶ (1, 8), (1, 11), (4, 11), (4, 8), (1, 8)

❷ (11, 6), (11, 9), (9, 11), (7, 9), (7, 6), (11, 6)

❸ (3, 5), (1, 2), (4, 2), (6, 5), (3, 5)

❹ (7, 0), (11, 0), (9, 3), (7, 0)

Give a set of coordinates that could be connected to form:

❺ a rectangle ______________________

❻ a hexagon ______________________

Drawing Views of Three-Dimensional Shapes

Introduction

Objective → Students represent three-dimensional shapes using two-dimensional drawings. Students build three-dimensional shapes from two-dimensional drawings.

Context → Students have studied the faces of three-dimensional shapes in terms of their two-dimensional characteristics. This is the first lesson in which students are asked to draw different views of a three-dimensional shape. They will continue working with this concept for another lesson. Then they will study more characteristics of three-dimensional shapes, such as volume.

NCTM Standards Focus

The standards call for students to be able to translate three-dimensional images into two-dimensional representations, and vice versa. In this standards-based lesson, students analyze a three-dimensional model, represent different views in two dimensions, and construct models of three-dimensional figures using connecting cubes. Students also make connections to other disciplines such as art and architecture.

Representation Students represent buildings in two-dimensional drawings and in three-dimensional models with connecting cubes. They learn how to use these representations to actually make the three-dimensional object.

Reasoning Students use their visual reasoning skills to determine how to make their representations of both the two-dimensional and three-dimensional figures.

Connections In this lesson, students note connections between two-dimensional and three-dimensional shapes. There is a strong connection made between the disciplines of art and architecture, and the drawing and modeling of the figures. In fact, students are actually doing, in a simplified fashion, what architects do.

Teaching Plan

Materials → Student pages 86–87 (about 8 copies of student page 86 per pair of students); connecting cubes (25–30 per pair); teacher's Models A and B (optional) made from connecting cubes (see Figure 1); a cloth large enough to cover teacher's models (optional); blank stickers; paper bags

Preparation → Make Models A and B (optional) from connecting cubes, as shown in Figure 1. Find a cloth big enough to cover one of the models completely.

Figure 1

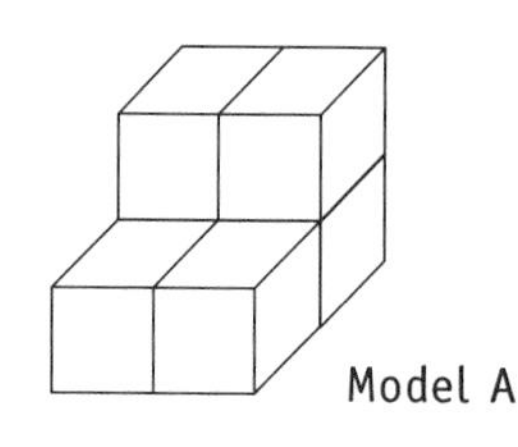

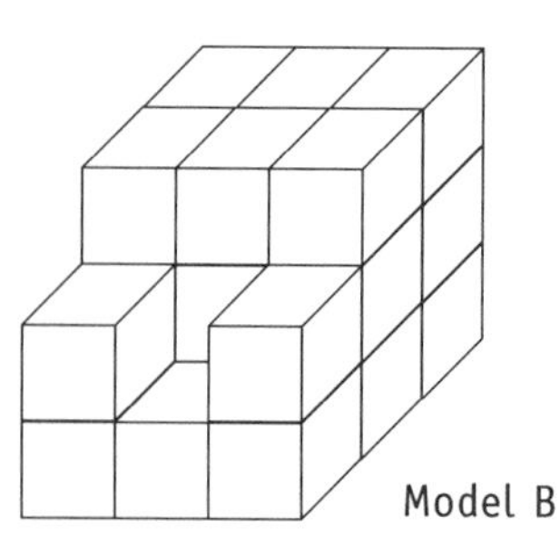

DISTRIBUTE 25–30 CONNECTING CUBES and about 8 copies of page 86 to each pair of students. Begin the lesson by telling students that today they will be exploring three-dimensional figures and their two-dimensional representations. Tell students that they will work in pairs to draw the faces of a model made from connecting cubes, and then replicate the model with cubes. They will design their own three-dimensional model, draw its two-dimensional faces, and challenge other students to replicate the model using only the drawings.

This lesson connects the representation of a three-dimensional object in a two-dimensional drawing. Take time to review the following with students so they understand this connection and its connection with art. While reviewing the concepts of two- and three-dimensional objects, discuss three-dimensional drawing (perspective rendering). A perspective rendering of a house or building (Figure 2) shows how a building looks to the human eye. Although the drawing is done on a two-dimensional surface, the artist uses special techniques, such as lines converging to a horizon point (perspective) and shading, to make the house look three-dimensional. These techniques use distortion to make the building in the painting appear realistic. The ground line and roofline of the house in Figure 2 converge to a vanishing point. On a real building, these lines would be fixed and parallel. A person could build a house by looking at a three-dimensional rendering, but it would be an approximation because the builder would have to guess at the actual dimensions and proportions of the house.

Architects use two-dimensional drawings or views of buildings (Figure 3) to show how that building exists in space. The two-dimensional views show the geometry of buildings. From them, a person can determine the exact proportions and dimensions of the building. Lines and sides that are parallel in the real object, are parallel in the drawing. From plans, a person can find out everything needed to construct the building. However, it takes practice to be able to read and understand these drawings, as they do not represent the objects as the eye normally sees them.

When the students are comfortable with the concepts of perspective and views, uncover one face of the model (Figure 4). Face 1 is the back face of the model.

Figure 2: Simple perspective

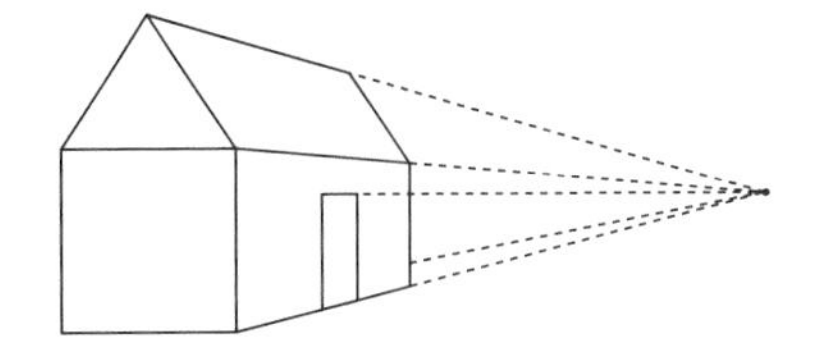

Figure 3: Elevation views

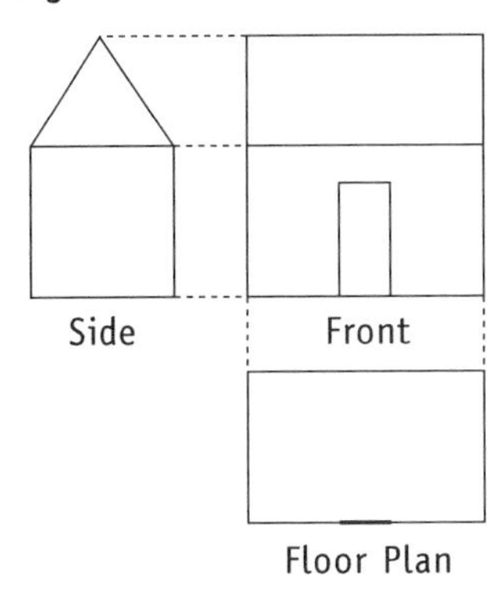

f.y.i.

Only one face of the model is shown to students at a time so that they can focus on the two-dimensional aspects of the face. This will help students make the connection between the three-dimensional object and its representation in two-dimensional drawings.

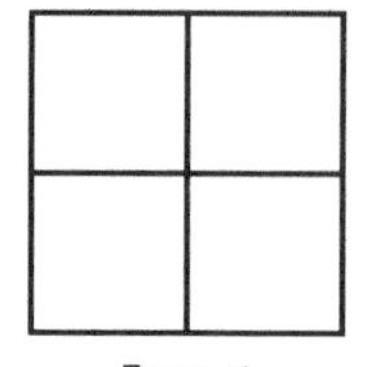

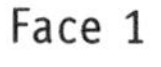

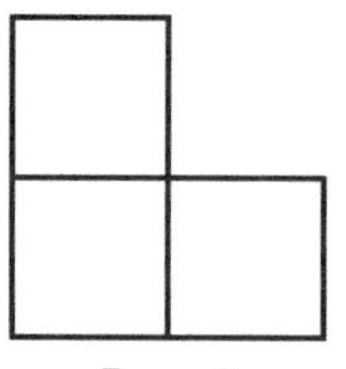

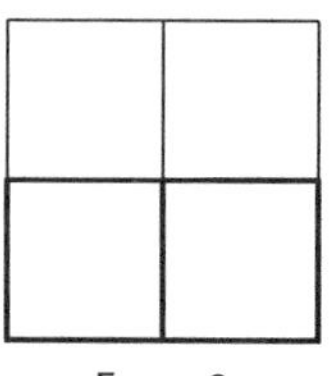

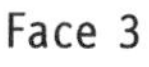

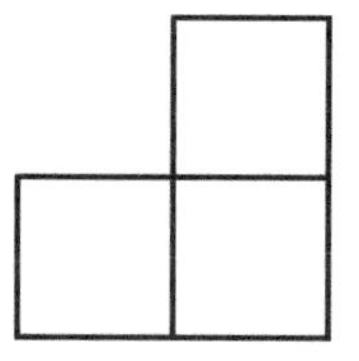

Face 4

Be sure to keep the rest of the model covered. Ask students to analyze the face. *What shape is the face? How many cubes is it made from? How could you show this face in a drawing? Why is grid paper helpful for making such a drawing?* Have students draw the face on the grid found on student page 86. Have students share their drawings.

Now have students build the face with cubes. Discuss the difference between the three-dimensional cube model they have just made and the drawing. Label the face on Model A with a sticker that says *front*. Have the students label their cube models the same way.

Keep the model covered but turn it 90 degrees to Face 2. Have students analyze this face of the cube. *Is this a face? What shape is this face? How many cubes are there? How does this face relate to the other face of the object that you just modeled?* If necessary, rotate the model back to Face 1 to let students see it again. Have them draw Face 2. Then ask them to add Face 2 to their cube model. Make sure that students understand that Face 2 is physically connected to Face 1 and shares a cube at the corner.

Repeat the process for Face 3. Students should have noticed when drawing Face 2 that one row of cubes is missing on the top layer. When drawing Face 3, this presents an interesting problem of how to represent this in a strictly two-dimensional format. Ask students to look carefully at the face. *What do you see when you look at it straight on?* When viewed straight on, the resulting drawing should show four cubes, similar to the drawing for Face 1. However, the setback cubes can be depicted somewhat differently. In an architectural rendering, this is indicated by making the lines darkest that are on the closest plane to the viewer. The lines on every plane behind the closest plane, are of a lighter weight. See the drawing of Face 3 in Figure 4. The setback cubes are rendered with a lighter line.

Repeat the process for Face 4. Reveal your model cube. Have students share and discuss their models.

Have students discuss the relationship between the model and the drawings. *What did covering all but one face of the model do to your view of the model? Can you build the model just from the drawings?*

If there is time, repeat the exercise with Model B (Figure 5). This time leave the model uncovered, but remind students that they must focus on just the face when making the two-dimensional drawing. When drawing Face 3, remind students to analyze the face carefully and decide how to use different line weights to indicate the irregularity of the face.

Now have students work in pairs to design and build their own three-dimensional cube model and then to draw four two-dimensional views of their model. When students have completed their drawings and model, have them put the model in a paper bag. Then have teams of students exchange drawings and try to build the other team's model with connecting cubes by using only their drawings. When the team thinks they have completed the model, have them compare it to the model in the bag.

Use student page 87 for classwork or homework.

Figure 5

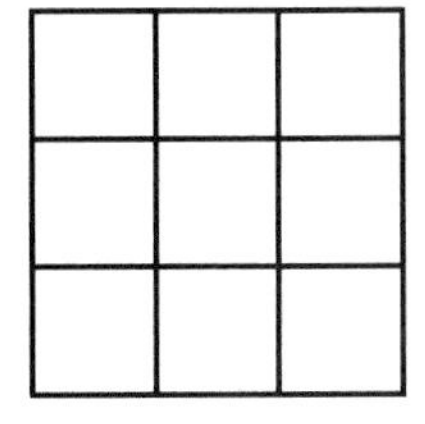
Face 1

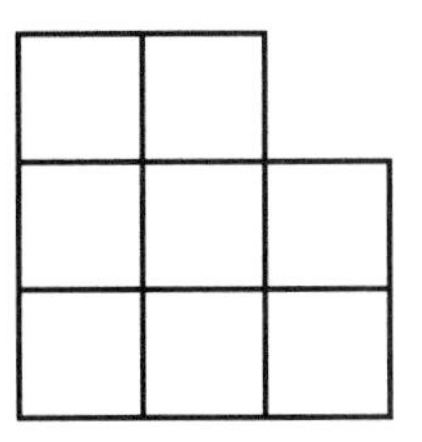
Face 2

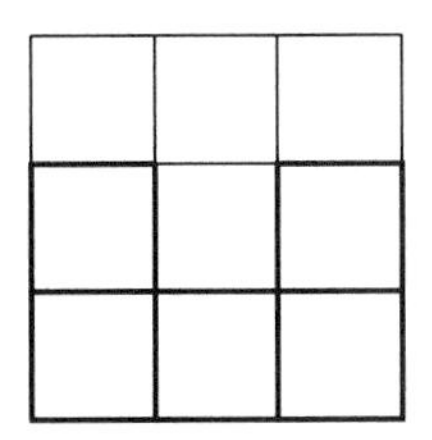
Face 3

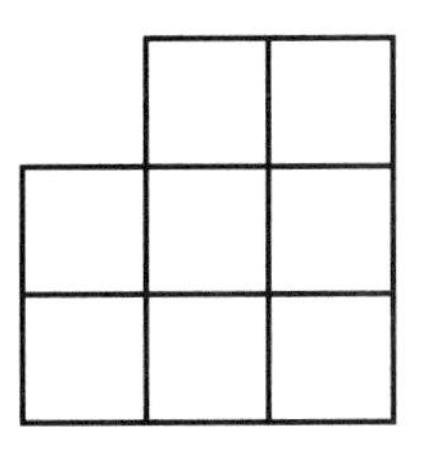
Face 4

Student Pages

Student page 86 provides grids for making the two-dimensional drawings of the three-dimensional model. Student page 87 presents two-dimensional drawings of a model and asks students to construct the model.

Assessment

You had the opportunity to assess students when they made their two-dimensional drawings and made models of each face. Because students worked one face at a time, you were able to use these assessments to make corrections in misunderstandings during the process, after a student had built the model. Additional opportunities for assessment were available in the subsequent activities and the student page.

NCTM Standards Summary

In this lesson students analyzed models of three-dimensional shapes made of connecting cubes. They made both two-dimensional and three-dimensional representations of the models, approaching the models face by face, and first drawing a face and then constructing it with connecting cubes. Students shared their reasoning and strategies as they showed their drawings and models to the class and explained what they had done. Students also used reasoning as they analyzed drawings of the faces of figures and then constructed models of the objects represented in the drawings.

Answers

Page 86
Answers are shown in Figures 4 and 5, pages 84 and 85.

Page 87
The figure is a stair-step shape with two cubes in the first row, four in the second, six in the last.

Name ______________________

Drawing Views of Three-Dimensional Shapes

Draw one view of the model in each part of the grid.

Name ______________________

Drawing Views of Three-Dimensional Shapes

Look at the four views. Make the model.

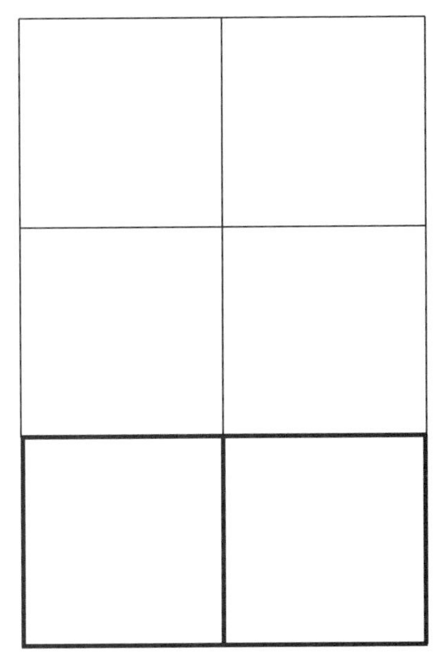

Face 1

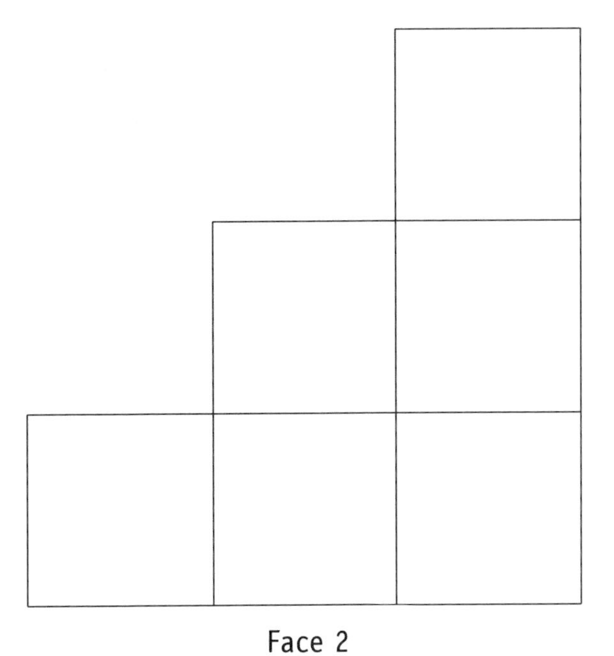

Face 2

Face 3

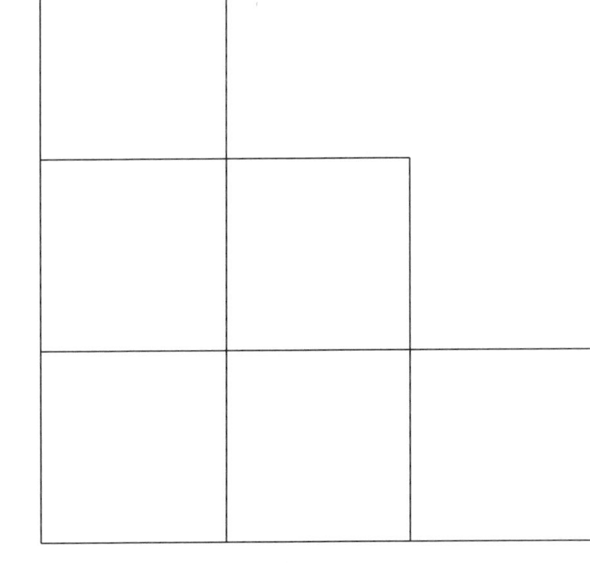

Face 4

Exploring Rotations

Introduction

Objective → Students will determine whether one figure is the turn image of another figure and will draw turn images.

Context → The lesson comes at the end of a geometry unit. Students have studied polygons and their attributes and have worked with reflections.

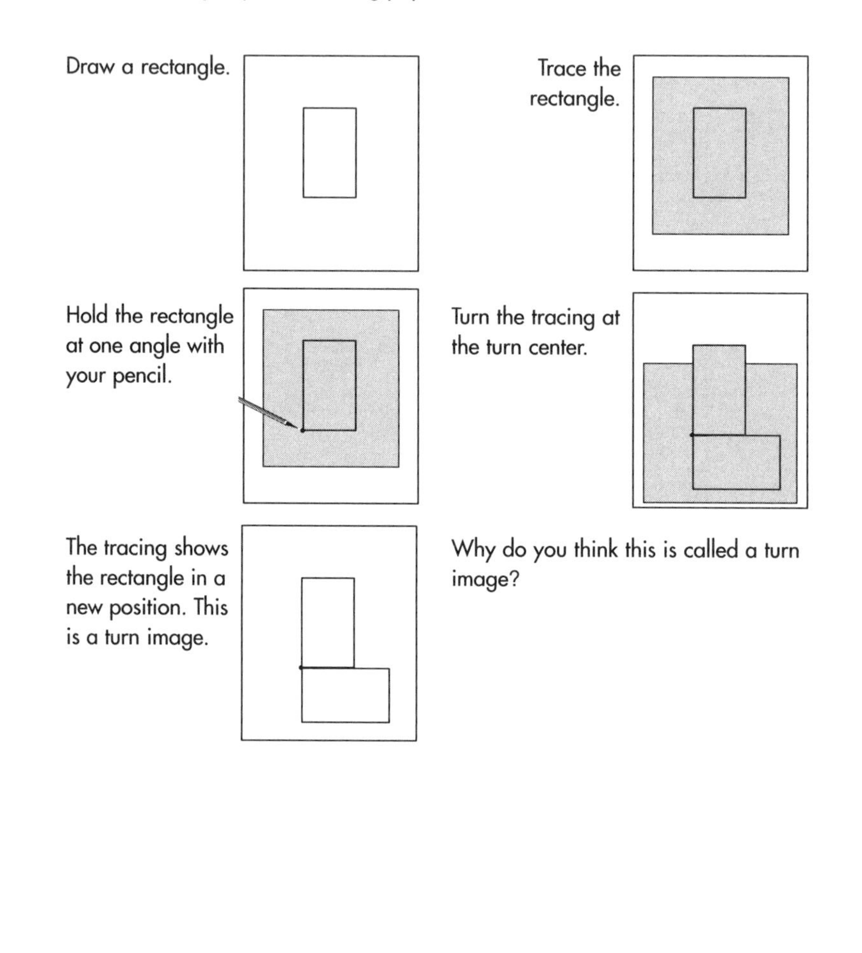

Exploring Rotations

Learn

Work in small groups. Use tracing paper.

Draw a rectangle.

Trace the rectangle.

Hold the rectangle at one angle with your pencil.

Turn the tracing at the turn center.

The tracing shows the rectangle in a new position. This is a turn image.

Why do you think this is called a turn image?

NCTM Process Standards Analysis and Focus

The standards analysis examines how the process standards have been incorporated into the above lesson. By increasing the focus on three of the process standards, a more effective and meaningful lesson can be presented. The suggestions offered can help you to think about how this might be accomplished.

Representation The lesson has students trace a shape they have drawn and turn the tracing. They also draw turns of shapes copied onto dot paper. Additionally, students identify the number of turns around a point represented by figures in drawings. While these activities are valid, turns around a point are not consistently represented.

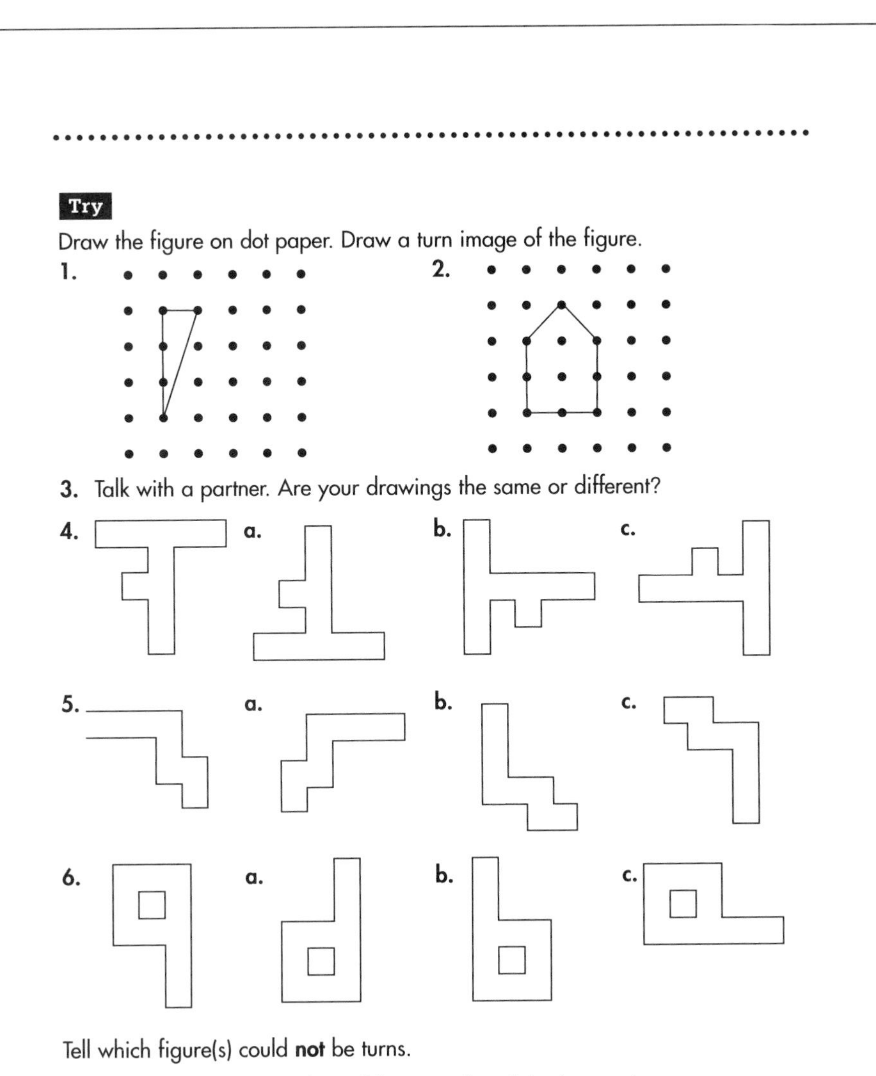

Suggestion → **Have students use physical objects, including their own bodies, to model rotations. Using concrete representations will allow students to view a greater range of turn positions, increase the accuracy of the resulting turns, and facilitate abstract thinking.**

Reasoning and Proof After turning shapes and tracing their turns, students compare their work with classmates. An exercise at the end of the lesson asks students to explain how they found their answer.

Suggestion → **Activate reasoning by having students visualize how they think turns of an object will look and then have them check their thinking. Looking for orientations of shapes that do not represent simple turns, and explaining why they do not, will reinforce understanding.**

Communication Most questions in the lesson require limited responses. A final question that asks students to explain how they determined their answers for the exercise provides an opportunity to explain thinking.

Suggestion → **Increase the focus on reasoning by having students explain their thinking to open up communication. Have students explain how they recognize turns to increase their ability to differentiate turns from other transformations, namely reflections and slides.**

Problem Solving Although identifying rotations involves reasoning, it does not lend itself to problem solving. Problem solving is not part of this lesson.

Connections Recognizing turns requires making connections between the shape of a figure and how it looks when it is rotated. The lesson does not introduce other connections.

The teaching plan that follows details how the suggestions made here for incorporating process standards can incorporated into the lesson. Before teaching the lesson you might want to prepare drawings of figures and their rotations (see page 91).

f.y.i.

Turning to the left on the right heel is more difficult to accomplish than turning to the right. If students try this turn, instruct them to first point their left foot to the left without moving their right foot. Then have them pivot toward the left on their right heel.

Revised Teaching Plan

Materials → Pattern blocks or other geometric shapes; tag board; paper; scissors; and prepared drawings (see page 93)

START THE LESSON WITH AN ACTIVITY in which students use their own bodies to represent rotations. Ask students to stand up and face the front of the room. Tell them that their right heel will represent a turning point. Have them keep their arms at their sides and concentrate on where their faces and their right and left arms are in relation to their desk, the front of the room, and what they can see without moving their heads.

Instruct students to turn on their right heels without lifting their right heel off the floor and face the wall to their right. *If you could look down on yourself from the ceiling, how would the positions of your head and arms have changed?* (Both location and direction faced by left arm are changed. Right arm is in the same location, but the direction it faces has changed. Right heel in the same location, but the foot is rotated, etc.) *Could you have reached this position by turning to the left instead of the right?* (Yes.) *Explain.* (You would have to turn a greater distance in order to reach the same position.) Have students turn to face the back of the room, the corner, and the left side of the room, each time asking students to describe the position of arms and face relative to their starting point. Then have students sit back down.

Guide students to understand the importance of identifying a point on a figure around which a turn is being made. Show Figures A and B on the overhead. Make sure the point of rotation is identified on each of the figures, but have figures separated as shown. *Does Figure B represent a turn of Figure A?* (No.) *How do you know?* (If the figure were rotated, the sides and angles would not line up.) *How could we prove that?* (By rotating the figure) *What might have been done?* (It might have been turned and flipped, or it might only have been flipped.) *How could we prove your answer?* (By trying both)

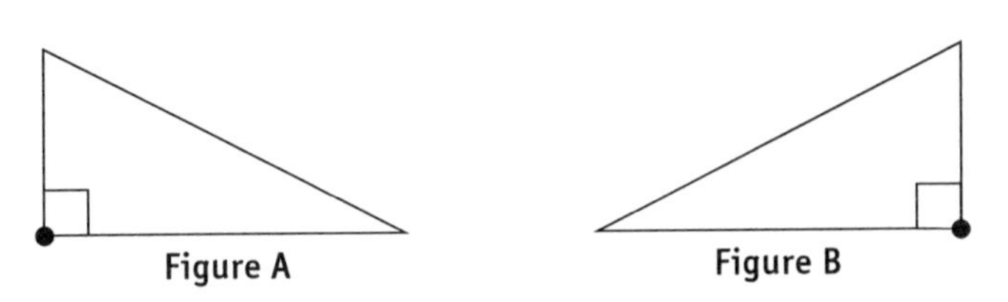
Figure A Figure B

DISTRIBUTE TAG BOARD and instruct students to cut out three or four geometric shapes to use as they investigate turns or rotations. Irregular shapes may prove easier to track than regular figures such as equilateral triangles, but students should investigate both types of shapes. If you prefer, provide students with a variety of manipulatives of different shapes and sizes.

f.y.i.

Regular figures are figures in which all sides are equal and all angles are equal.

Next, tell students to select one of their shapes to use. Have them draw a dot on a sheet of paper to represent the point around which they will rotate the shape they are using. Tell them to be sure to identify a point on their shape to align with that dot as they rotate the shape. *That point on your shape is called the point of rotation. Why do you think mathematicians call it that?*

HAVE STUDENTS TRACE THEIR SHAPE and consider the tracing as the starting point for a rotation. Encourage them to visualize a turn of their shape and draw what they picture in their minds. Then have them check their thinking by rotating the actual shape. *Would turning to the left rather than the right change the result? Explain.* (If you turn far enough in either direction, you will create the same result.)

What Might Happen . . . What to Do

Students might think that merely sliding the shape around a point produces a turn. Emphasize the importance of keeping the rotation point of the shape aligned with the point around which the rotation takes place. The relationship between parts of the figure to the rotation point must remain the same throughout the turn. You might have students compare the two drawings shown. The drawing at the left appears to be a slide. Point out how the orientation of the letter changes relative to the rotation point; it remains right side up. The drawing on the right correctly illustrates a turn of the letter.

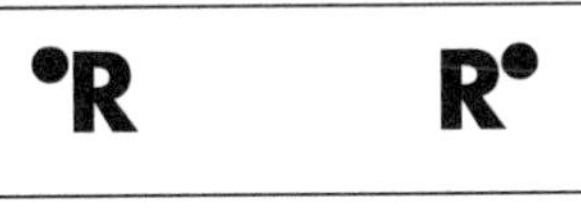

Sliding the figure around or through the point.

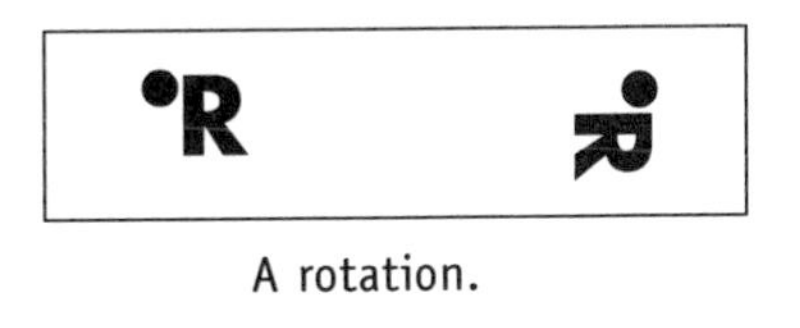

A rotation.

f.y.i.

When transformations are applied to symmetrical figures, it can be very difficult to identify what has occurred; the result of a rotation and a flip might look the same. Having students label the vertices of symmetrical figures as they make their drawings may provide some help in figuring out what transformations have taken place. Comparing rotations of asymmetrical forms with those of symmetrical shapes will also demonstrate this point.

NOW DIRECT STUDENTS to show a rotation in different stages. Instruct them to rotate a figure around a point and select four different positions of that rotation to trace. Suggest they trace their shape as they start and then trace four additional turns. *Are there orientations of your shape that could represent something other than a turn? How do you know?* Invite students to show the starting position and draw an orientation that does not represent a turn. Labeling vertices in the drawings will make the outcome easier to see.

Alter the manner in which students evaluate rotations by having them examine drawings to discern whether one drawing could be a rotation of another. Instruct students to work with a classmate and make pairs of drawings with which to quiz their partner. Tell each partner to select a shape and make a pair of drawings for that shape. For the first drawing of the pair, students should trace a starting position but not mark any point of rotation on the figure or on the paper. That figure should be labeled *A*. Students may then recreate the same figure using any combination of moves they choose in another location on the paper, trace the transformation, and label it *B*. Again, no rotation points should be identified.

INSTRUCT PARTNERS TO EXCHANGE papers and identify what has occurred for each pair of drawings. *Could drawing* B *be a rotation of drawing* A? *What strategies will you use to help determine whether a rotation, or turn, is represented? If not a turn, can you identify what could have been done? How will you prove your answer?* As partners identify what each other's pairs of drawings represent, instruct them to justify their decisions in writing on a separate sheet of paper. Both the point of rotation for the figure and how they decided whether a drawing represented a turn or something else should be included in the explanation. Partners can check each other's papers before you collect them.

If time permits, have students repeat the activity. If they used a symmetrical figure for their first pair of drawings, have them use an asymmetrical figure for their second pair of drawings. Select pairs of figures to present to the class for identification. An alternative would be to duplicate pairs of figures for students to identify as additional practice in a follow-up activity.

End with a class exercise to summarize the lesson. Before class, prepare a transparency for the overhead or a poster showing several pairs of figures similar to those created in the student activities above. Make some pairs of figures clearly represent rotations about the same marked point, and other pairs showing rotations, flips, and/or slides away from the marked point.

Show one pair of figures at a time and ask students to decide if the second figure in the pair could have been drawn from the first by doing only a turn around a point of rotation. Instruct students to show thumbs up if they think the answer is *yes,* thumbs down if they think the answer is *no*. Encourage students to explain their thinking.

Student Pages

Students should now be able to complete exercises similar to those on the reduced student pages. You might consider asking students to give short explanations of what was done to figures they identify as not representing simple rotations.

Assessment

Reviewing students' written responses to their partner's drawings enabled you to assess their thinking as the lesson developed. Observing students during the class exploration and listening to their explanations provided additional opportunities for assessing their understanding of rotations.

NCTM Standards Summary

Using concrete representations allowed students to see how figures look when they are rotated around a point. The reasoning required to distinguish figure pairs that were simply rotated from those which had undergone additional changes gave students a hands-on process-based understanding of this concept. The communication resulting from the partner activity and class discussion and the explanations given during the class exercise increased students' involvement and helped clarify and strengthen understanding.

f.y.i.

Having students show thumbs up or down offers them a chance to communicate their decisions quickly and easily. It also enables you to get a quick read of students' thinking while getting a general assessment of the understanding of the class as whole. To discourage students who are unsure from waiting to see what others do, you might want to encourage students to keep their signaling thumb close to their chests.

Standard 4 **Measurement**

AT THE FOURTH GRADE LEVEL, measurement includes a lot of work with measuring length using customary and metric units, converting between metric units, and finding volume. Our lessons are derived from these important topics. They include a lesson on understanding the relationships between the customary measures of inch, foot, and yard, a lesson on converting metric units to make comparisons, a lesson that uses cubes to determine volume, and a lesson on estimating length using metric units.

Three lessons model how the process standards can be used to teach content. A fourth lesson is a hypothetical textbook lesson that we have revised to be more standards based. These four lessons do not represent the entire curriculum, but rather provide glimpses of how, with a more concentrated effort to incorporate the process standards, better mathematics teaching and learning can be achieved.

One lesson we have chosen focuses students on the customary units of length: inch, foot, and yard. In this lesson, students measure objects using all three units, then decide which unit is the most appropriate for that object. By using reasoning and proof and communication, students develop a better sense of the three customary units.

Another lesson we have chosen has students convert metric measures of length between meters, centimeters, and millimeters. By incorporating the process standards of connections, reasoning and proof, and problem solving, students think about how the conversions make sense, and use the conversions to solve problems in which comparisons of metric measures are made.

A third lesson we have chosen has students using cubes to determine the volume of a rectangular solid. Instead of just being presented with a formula, students use cubes to build representations of rectangular solids. Students use these to make connections, and use reasoning to predict the volumes of other rectangular solids.

The hypothetical textbook lesson we have chosen to revise is one in which students work on estimating lengths using metric units. Through better incorporation of the process standards of representation, communication, and reasoning and proof, students are able to discuss their reasons for their estimates. They refine their thinking and learn ways that other students develop their estimates. Students check their estimates by measuring.

Standard 4 Lessons

Understanding Inch, Foot, and Yard

Converting Among Metric Units

Using Cubes to Determine Volume

Estimating Metric Units of Length

Understanding Inch, Foot, and Yard

Introduction

Objective → Students will be able to measure in inches, feet, and yards. They will determine which measure is most appropriate for a given situation.

Context → Students have worked with both standard and nonstandard units of linear measurement and have been introduced to the measures *inch, foot,* and *yard.* They will go on to solve problems requiring the use of units of measurement.

NCTM Standards Focus

Traditionally, once students understand the necessity of using standard units, they are expected to apply this understanding and to answer measurement conversion questions. In this standards-based lesson, students are actively engaged in measuring relevant classroom lengths, heights, and distances using three customary units of measure. By applying reasoning and proof to determine the most appropriate unit of measure and by communicating their rationale for selecting a certain measure, students grapple with each unit of measure and build their own understanding.

Communication Students work in pairs to measure a selection of classroom objects. They discuss which unit (inches, feet, or yards) most appropriately communicates the measurement for each item. They also communicate with one another the rationale for selecting one measure over another.

Reasoning and Proof Students constantly apply reasoning skills as they determine which unit of measure is most appropriate for a given situation. By conducting and recording actual measurements, they can compare their results to prove which makes the most sense.

Teaching Plan

Materials → Student pages 100–101; yardsticks; inch/foot rulers; classroom objects

WITH YOUR STUDENTS, create a list of 6 objects and 6 distances they could measure in the classroom. Make sure that 2 or 3 of the objects or distances are greater than a few yards long (e.g., the width of the classroom) and a few others are less than a foot long. Also, try not to include too many of the objects or distances listed on student page 101.

Assign each student a partner and pass out an inch/foot ruler to each pair of students. Review the inch unit with them. Point out the markings for $\frac{1}{4}$, $\frac{1}{2}$, and $\frac{3}{4}$ inch. Explain that when they measure using inches, they should record their measures to the nearest $\frac{1}{4}$ inch. Hold up your ruler. *How long is the ruler?* (12 inches, 1 foot) *How many inches are in $\frac{1}{4}$ foot?* (3) *$\frac{1}{2}$ foot?* (6) *$\frac{3}{4}$ foot?* (9) Make certain that students understand this relationship. They will be using a similar understanding when measuring in feet to record their measurements to the nearest $\frac{1}{4}$ foot.

After working with the ruler, hold up a yardstick. Point out that the yardstick (1 yard) is equal to 36 inches, or 3 feet. *If a yard is equal to 36 inches, how many inches would $\frac{1}{4}$ yard be?* (9 inches) *How many feet would $\frac{1}{2}$ yard be? How many inches?* ($1\frac{1}{2}$ feet, or 18 inches). *How many inches is $\frac{3}{4}$ yard?* (27 inches) When measuring in yards, students will record their measurements to the nearest $\frac{1}{4}$ yard.

Select a couple of objects or distances and demonstrate how to measure each using the three different units. Be sure to give special attention to measuring to the nearest $\frac{1}{4}$ foot and $\frac{1}{4}$ yard. Point out to students that when measuring in feet and yards they will most likely have to record an approximate measurement, rounding to the nearest $\frac{1}{4}$ foot or yard. For example, an object measuring 29 inches would be recorded as $2\frac{1}{2}$ feet and $\frac{3}{4}$ yard.

Hand out student page 100. Tell students to select 8 of the objects or distances from the list of 12 you posted and record them on their sheets. They should then measure each object or distance to the nearest $\frac{1}{4}$ inch, $\frac{1}{4}$ foot, and $\frac{1}{4}$ yard and record their measurements on the sheet. While students work on measuring the objects and distances they chose, observe the different approaches and strategies they use to complete the task.

Methods Students Might Use

- Measure each item three times, first in inches (ruler), next in feet (ruler), and finally in yards (yardstick).
- Use either a yardstick or ruler to measure only in inches, then calculate the measurements in feet and yards by applying the relationships between the measures.
- Select what they think is the most appropriate unit, then measure the item once. Convert to determine the other two measures.

ENCOURAGE STUDENTS TO COMMUNICATE with their partners and with other groups their strategies for completing their measurements. These strategies may change as they measure different objects and identify methods that are more accurate or seem more efficient. Regularly ask students, *What is the most appropriate measure for this object? Why?* Students should be using both their communication and their reasoning skills to choose appropriate measurement units and to discuss their strategies with each other.

After students have recorded their measurements, have student pairs share their results. When a particular object or distance yields differing student responses, select one pair of students to demonstrate their method for measuring this particular object or distance. Use this demonstration to lead students through a questioning process that helps them to reach consensus on the measurements. This is another area in which students will work with the standards of communication and reasoning and proof.

PAIR STUDENTS UP AGAIN, this time with new partners, and pass out student page 101. Provide each pair with an inch/foot ruler and a yardstick. Explain that this time around, they are to first select what they feel to be the most appropriate unit of measure for the object or distance listed on the sheet, then measure and record their findings.

What Might Happen . . . What to Do

Students might want to measure first, rather than determine which unit is most appropriate. Have students decide on a unit of measure before actually conducting their measurements. Encourage them to look at the relative length of the object to select what they feel would be the best unit of measure.

GO OVER THE RESULTS of this measuring exercise with the entire class. Students may end up with slightly different measurements for some of the objects or distances (e.g., length of a shoe), but there should be some consistency in their selection of the most appropriate unit of measure. When students disagree on what is the most appropriate measure to use for a particular object or distance, encourage them to explain their reasoning. Although there are no single "correct" units of measure for a given object or distance, students should be able to explain why the unit of measure they selected makes the most sense to them.

Conclude the lesson by having students share their responses to the question at the bottom of page 101 and discuss the reasoning behind their responses.

Student Pages

Student page 100 provides a place for students to list the eight objects or distances they choose for this activity. They also record their measurements for three different units of measurement to the nearest $\frac{1}{4}$ unit. Student page 101 instructs students to choose the most appropriate unit of measure and then find the actual measurements of ten objects and distances. The final written question assesses students' ability to apply their understanding to a relevant, real-world example.

Assessment

You observed students as they completed measurement tasks using units of length. You listened to them communicate their understandings and strategies. You listened to their reasoning as they described which unit of measure was most appropriate for a given situation. You then assessed their ability to transfer this reasoning process to a new situation where they first selected an appropriate unit of measure, then measured ten different objects or distances.

NCTM Standards Summary

In this lesson, students conducted measurements of several different objects and/or distances using inches, feet, and yards. They first looked closely at each of these measures to identify how they are related to one another. They then applied reasoning and proof to determine the most appropriate unit of measurement for a particular measuring task. They communicated their reasoning process and the results they obtained and used what they learned from these discussions to adapt their own strategies and methods.

Answers

Page 100

Student choices of objects or distances to measure will vary.

Page 101

1. Feet or inches
2. Inches
3. Feet or inches
4. Feet or yards
5. Inches
6. Feet or yards
7. Feet or yards
8. Feet or inches
9. Feet or inches
10. Inches or feet
11. Feet. Most pool depths are between 3 and 10 feet. This is too many for inches and two few for yards.

Name

Understanding Inch, Foot, and Yard

Measurement Hunt

Select 8 objects or distances from the class list to measure. Write each object or distance you choose in the first column. Record your measurements in each unit, then circle what you think is the most appropriate measure.

Object	Length in Inches	Length in Feet	Length in Yards	Most Appropriate Measure
				in. ft yd
				in. ft yd
				in. ft yd
				in. ft yd
				in. ft yd
				in. ft yd
				in. ft yd
				in. ft yd

Name ____________________

Understanding Inch, Foot, and Yard

Using Appropriate Measures

Circle the most appropriate measure, then measure each object or distance and record your results.

Object	Most Appropriate Measure	Actual Measurement (to nearest $\frac{1}{4}$ unit)
❶ Height of student desk	in. ft yd	
❷ Length of shoe	in. ft yd	
❸ Height from heel to knee	in. ft yd	
❹ Distance across classroom	in. ft yd	
❺ Length of index finger	in. ft yd	
❻ Width of chalkboard	in. ft yd	
❼ Distance from desk to door	in. ft yd	
❽ Height of chair seat	in. ft yd	
❾ Length of arm span	in. ft yd	
❿ Width of math book	in. ft yd	

⓫ Which would be the best unit for measuring the depth of water in a swimming pool? Explain your reasoning.

____

____

Converting Among Metric Units

Introduction

Objective → Students will be able to convert among meters, centimeters, and millimeters, and use these conversions to solve comparison problems.

Context → Students have used both customary and metric units in measurement. They will go on to develop and refine their use of both metric and customary units of measure.

NCTM Standards Focus

Students are often taught that metric units of measure are related to one another by factors of 10. They may not, however, have had opportunities to focus on understanding the patterns involved or the operations needed to convert between larger and smaller units. This standards-based lesson focuses students' attention on understanding the connections between metric units and factors of 10 and on using multiplication and division to convert between units.

Connections Students make connections between factors of 10 and converting from one unit of metric measure to another. They connect the operation of multiplication to converting from a larger unit to a smaller unit. They connect division to converting from a smaller unit to a larger one. Connections are also made to the relationships between customary units.

Reasoning and Proof Students begin to recognize the patterns inherent in metric conversions and to apply these patterns to converting between units. They are also able to apply their reasoning to complete more complex conversions.

Problem Solving Students use their conversion skills to solve a variety of problems.

Teaching Plan

Materials → Student pages 106–107; metric rulers; meter sticks

BEGIN THE LESSON BY reviewing with students the relationship between the number of feet and the number of inches. Students should know that the length of 1 foot is the same as the length of 12 inches and that the length of 2 feet is the same as the length of 24 inches. *Which is the greater unit of measure?* (Feet) *Are more feet or more inches required to measure the same length?* (More inches) *What conclusion can we draw from this?* (To measure the same length, you need more of a smaller unit.) This is a key idea for students and using units that students are familiar with will help them make the connection that this relationship holds with metric units as well.

Ask students to list some of the metric units that they know. If they list others besides ones for length, ask them further to identify from their list the units that measure length. Ask students if they know how long 1 meter is. (A little longer than a yard or a little longer than 3 feet) Show students a meter stick so they get a mental image of the length of a meter.

Ask students if they know how long a centimeter is. Students should know that a centimeter is a relatively short unit of length. (The buttons on a touch-tone phone are about 1 centimeter wide.) Show students the meter stick again, and show them one centimeter. *To measure the same length, would you need more meters or more centimeters?* (More centimeters) Make the connection back to feet and inches—you need more of the smaller unit to measure the same length. Ask students if they know how many centimeters it takes to make one meter. (100) Students can count along the meter stick to verify this for themselves.

Ask students if they know how long one millimeter is. Students should know that a millimeter is a very short unit of length. Show students the meter stick again, and show them one centimeter. Then show them one millimeter. *To measure the same length, would you need more centimeters or more millimeters?* (More millimeters) Point out that now centimeters is the larger unit. Ask students if they know how many millimeters it takes to make one centimeter. (10) Students can count along the meter stick or a metric ruler to verify this for themselves.

Summarize these results on the board. *Which of the three units—meter, centimeter, millimeter—is the longest?* (Meter) *Which is the next longest?* (Centimeter) *How many centimeters are in one meter?* (100) *Which unit is the shortest?* (Millimeter) *How many millimeters are in one centimeter?* (10)

CONTINUE THE LESSON by asking students some basic conversion questions. Show students two meter sticks, end-to-end. *How many centimeters is this?* (200) Add a third meter stick. *How many centimeters is this?* (300) Write these results on the board.

Show students one centimeter and reestablish that this is 10 millimeters. Now show students two centimeters. *How many millimeters is this?* (20) Now show students three centimeters. *How many millimeters is this?* (30)

Show students 10 centimeters. *How many millimeters is this?* (100). Write these results on the board.

Show students the meter stick again, and tell them that it represents 100 centimeters. *How many millimeters is it?* (1000) Show students two meter sticks. *How many millimeters is it?* (2000)

HAVE STUDENTS GENERALIZE from these results. *How can you convert from a number of meters to the equivalent number of centimeters?* (Multiply by 100.) *How can you convert from a number of centimeters to the equivalent number of millimeters?* (Multiply by 10.) As a bonus, you might ask *How can you convert from a number of meters to the equivalent number of millimeters?* (Multiply by 1000.)

Now have students try some reverse conversions. *If a measure is 100 centimeters, how many meters is it?* (1) Now show two meter sticks. *We know this is 200 centimeters. How many meters is it?* (2) *If a measure was 800 centimeters, how many meters would it be?* (8)

If a measure is 40 millimeters, how many centimeters is it? (4) *If a measure is 90 millimeters, how many centimeters is it?* (9) *If a measure is 200 millimeters, how many centimeters is it?* (20)

Have students generalize from these results. *How can you convert from a number of centimeters to the equivalent number of meters?* (Divide by 100.) *How can you convert from a number of millimeters to the equivalent number of centimeters?* (Divide by 10.) As a bonus, you might ask *How can you convert from a number of millimeters to the equivalent number of meters?* (Divide by 1000.)

NOW POSE THIS PROBLEM to the students: *Joe's frog jumped 8 meters. Fred's frog jumped 900 centimeters. Whose frog jumped farther? By how much?* Ask students what they think they have to do to solve the problem. Be sure to discuss, that in order to compare the distances, the units have to be the same, whether meters or centimeters. Students can convert 8 meters to 800 centimeters and know that Fred's frog jumped farther by 100 centimeters, or they can convert 900 centimeters to 9 meters and know that Fred's frog jumped farther by 1 meter.

What Might Happen . . . What to Do

Students might just compare the two numbers, disregarding the units. Ask students which they would prefer to have: 3 dollars or 30 cents. If they say 3 dollars, ask them why—30 is more than 3. This emphasizes the importance of knowing the units, which is important in any comparison.

Allow students to work in pairs. Give each student a copy of student page 106. As you observe students at work, be sure that they realize that they have to convert so that the measures are expressed in the same unit before a valid comparison can be made. Discuss the results as a class.

In the first problem, for example, students could have converted 15 centimeters to 150 millimeters, and seen that this was 10 millimeters longer than the 140 millimeters, or students could have converted 140 millimeters to 14 centimeters, and seen that this was 1 centimeter shorter than the 15 centimeters. The other problems may be worked out similarly.

Student Pages

Student page 106 provides four problems for students to work on during class. Student page 107 includes more practice problems.

Assessment

You were able to assess students' understanding of equivalent measures and observe as they developed an understanding of converting between measures. Students' responses as they participated in the class discussion provided insight into their progress toward the objective. You were able to assess students' use of their conversion skills as you observed them complete the problems and listened to their solution methods.

NCTM Standards Summary

In this lesson, students practiced converting among metric measures. They made connections to relationships between units of measure in both customary and metric measurement systems. Students used reasoning to generalize the concepts of converting among units and applied these ideas in problem-solving situations.

Answers

Page 106

1. Alan's car; by 1 centimeter or 10 millimeters
2. Keiko; by 10 meters or 1000 centimeters
3. Ben's; by 2 centimeters or 20 millimeters
4. The first gymnast; by 900 centimeters or 9 meters

Page 107

1. More
2. Fewer
3. 500
4. 7
5. 6
6. 900
7. 400 millimeters; by 320 millimeters or 32 centimeters
8. The tennis ball; by 5 meters or 500 centimeters
9. 230 centimeters or 2300 millimeters

Name

Converting Among Metric Units

1. Alan's car rolled 15 centimeters.
Juan's car rolled 140 millimeters.
Whose car rolled farther? By how much?

2. Keiko can run 40 meters in 5 seconds. Marissa can run 3000 centimeters in 5 seconds. Who can run farther in 5 seconds? By how much?

3. Ben and Maria each measured a different line segment. Ben's was 80 millimeters long and Maria's was 6 centimeters long.
Whose segment was longer? By how much?

4. One gymnast walked on her hands a distance of 10 meters. Another gymnast walked on her hands a distance of 100 centimeters. Which gymnast walked farther on her hands? By how much?

Name ____________________

Converting Among Metric Units

Fill in the blank with *more* or *fewer*.

1. For measures of the same length, there will be ____________ centimeters than meters.

2. For measures of the same length, there will be ____________ centimeters than millimeters.

Perform each conversion.

3. 5 meters is the same measure as __________ centimeters.

4. 70 millimeters is the same measure as __________ centimeters.

5. 600 centimeters is the same measure as __________ meters.

6. 90 centimeters is the same measure as __________ millimeters.

Solve each problem.

7. Two sides of a rectangle measure 8 centimeters and 400 millimeters. Which side is longer? By how much?

8. A rubber ball bounced 15 meters into the air. A tennis ball bounced 2000 centimeters into the air. Which ball bounced higher? By how much?

9. The three sides of a triangle measure 1 meter, 80 centimeters, and 500 millimeters. What is the perimeter of the triangle?

© Creative Publications Permission is given by the publisher to reproduce this page for classroom or home use only.

Using Cubes to Determine Volume

Introduction

Objective → Students will estimate and determine the volume of rectangular solids using cubic units.

Context → Students have had experiences measuring volume with both nonstandard and standard units of measure. They will go on to learn and apply the formula for finding the volume of a rectangular solid.

f.y.i.

You may use either centimeters or inches as the basic unit for this lesson.

NCTM Standards Focus

Traditionally, students are presented with the formula $V = lwh$ for finding the volume of rectangular solids and are expected to apply it to a set of labeled figures. In this standards-based lesson, students physically represent volume by filling containers or building models using cubic units. This activity enables students to test and identify methods for finding volume.

Representation Students use combinations of cubes to represent the volume of various rectangular solids. The objects provide a physical representation of the volume.

Reasoning and Proof Students measure rectangular solid figures and use the measurements to help decide volume. By filling containers and building models, this concrete representation of volume helps students predict and prove the volume of various rectangular prisms.

Connections Students make connections between linear measurement and volume of rectangular prisms.

Teaching Plan

Materials → Student pages 112–113; rulers; cubes; 8 small rectangular prism containers or blocks whose width, length, and height are a whole number of units, labeled A–H

Preparation → Build various rectangular prisms from manila paper.

HOLD UP ONE OF THE RECTANGULAR prisms and review the process for finding its length, width, and height. Use a ruler to demonstrate, and write the dimensions on the board.

Ask students to share their experiences with exploring volume. You may want to remind them of filling containers with nonstandard units such as beans or rice. *What did you discover when you filled containers with items that were irregular in shape? Were you able to determine the volume accurately?* Students will most likely respond that they could not accurately determine volume using objects that didn't fill all the space inside a container. Point out that this is very important when determining volume—all the space within the object must be accounted for.

© Creative Publications

What kind of unit could you use to measure volume that would account for all empty space? Give students a chance to respond and explain their reasoning. If no one offers the idea of a cubic unit, hold up a cube. *What can you say about this cube?* Students might say that each face is square, and that it would fit in a corner of a box. Introduce the term *cubic centimeter* or *cubic inch,* and show them how to write it.

Hold up the rectangular prism you measured earlier. Ask students if they have an idea of its volume—*how many cubic units would fit inside?* Record their estimates, being sure to include the unit. Build or fill one layer. *Can you see a connection between the cubes filling the bottom of this box and the measurements we made of the box?* See if students are ready to note that the array of cubes has the same dimensions as the box.

At this point, ask students if they want to change their estimate of how many cubic units are in the rectangular prism. If so, record their revised estimates, and discuss why they changed their minds.

Ask students if they could fill the whole container with blocks. Have volunteers add one layer at a time until students agree that the container is full or that the block of cubes is the same size as the rectangular prism. *Do the cubes now fill all the space of this box? If you count the cubes, what will you have?* (The volume of the box) Have a volunteer help you count all the cubes and record the volume on the board, in cubic units. *How close is the actual volume to the estimates? Why do you think that is so?*

Arrange students in groups of two or three and pass out student page 112. Have the students record the letter of the rectangular prism you just measured, their estimate in cubic inches or cubic centimeters, then the actual number of cubes needed to find the volume in the same unit.

Provide each group with another one of the containers or blocks and a generous supply of cubes. Explain that they are going to estimate and measure the volumes of several more rectangular prisms and record them on the page. Rotate the prisms to each group. Observe the different approaches and strategies they use to estimate volume.

© Creative Publications

Methods Students Might Use

- Measure the dimensions of a rectangular prism and attempt to use these measurements to arrive at an estimate of its volume.
- Measure the dimensions, then fill or build the bottom layer of the prism, using this as a benchmark for their estimation.
- Measure the dimensions, then fill or build just the perimeter of the prism and use the number of cubes to arrive at a reasonable estimate.
- Make an estimate based only on looking at the prism.

While you observe the various strategies that students employ, circulate from group to group posing the following questions:

- *What connections can you make between the dimensions of Box B and the number of cubes needed for the bottom layer?*
- *How can you use the number of cubes in the bottom layer and the number of cubes in the height to make a reasonable estimate of the volume?*
- *Can you see a way you could find the volume if you didn't have cubes to work with? Explain what you would do.*

The objective of this questioning is to help students make connections between the dimensions of the object, the volume of the base or bottom layer, and the number of layers needed to fill all empty space in the object. Do not force these connections; rather lead the students to discover them through your questioning. They will arrive at their own understanding.

Once students have finished, display all the prisms on a table. Select one at a time to discuss. For each prism, record the students' estimates and ask a few students to share the strategies they used. Then record the measured volumes. Resolve any discrepancies in the results.

Select three objects and ask students to demonstrate how they might find the volume if they had only enough cubes to fill the bottom layer and one corner of the object.

ALLOW STUDENTS TO WORK in pairs on student page 113. Provide each pair with a ruler and a supply of 50 cubes. Have students first estimate the volume for each pictured rectangular prism, and record that number. Then have them build a model to check their estimates, and record the number of cubic units used. For the Challenge problem, students are to

© Creative Publications

prove what the volume is without building a model. Remind students to always record volume in cubic units.

Once students have completed this page, go over their results. Emphasize the reasoning skills and strategies they used to formulate estimates as well as find actual volume measurements. Give special attention to the Challenge problem, and allow students to demonstrate their strategies. Encourage them to share the different methods they employed.

Bring closure to the lesson by having several students explain how they would use cubes to first estimate, then find, the volume of a rectangular prism, while the other students tell whether they agree or disagree and why.

Student Pages

Student page 112 is a recording sheet for estimates and measures of the volumes of rectangular prisms. Student page 113 shows four rectangular prisms and asks students to reason what the volume is for each, then use cubes to prove their idea. A Challenge problem asks them to find the volume of a rectangular prism without using a physical representation.

Assessment

While students explored ways to find the volume of rectangular prisms, you observed them measuring the dimensions and using the measures to estimate volume. You watched them use cubes to fill space or build models to help them with their estimates, and then to find the actual volume of given prisms. You noted whether they made connections among the number of cubes needed to fill the bottom layer, number of cubes in height, and the volume of the prism.

NCTM Standards Summary

Students used cubes to represent the volumes of different rectangular solids. They applied reasoning skills as they formulated estimates of volume of different rectangular prisms and proved concretely the actual volumes. Through repeated experience with cubes, students made connections between volume and areas of base and height.

Answers

Page 112
Answers will vary.

Page 113

1. 24 cu. cm (or 24 cu. in.)
2. 36 cu. cm (or 36 cu. in.)
3. 30 cu. cm (or 30 cu. in.)
4. 48 cu. cm (or 48 cu. in.)
5. Estimates will vary. Volume is 100 cu. cm (or 100 cu. in.).

© Creative Publications

Name

Using Cubes to Determine Volume

Write the letter of each rectangular solid. Estimate the volume. Then use cubes to find the actual volume. Record these in cubic units.

Object	Estimate	Actual
1		
2		
3		
4		
5		
6		
7		
8		

© Creative Publications Permission is given by the publisher to reproduce this page for classroom or home use only.

Name ______________________________

Using Cubes to Determine Volume

Look at each figure. Tell what you think the volume is. Build a model with cubes to find the actual volume.

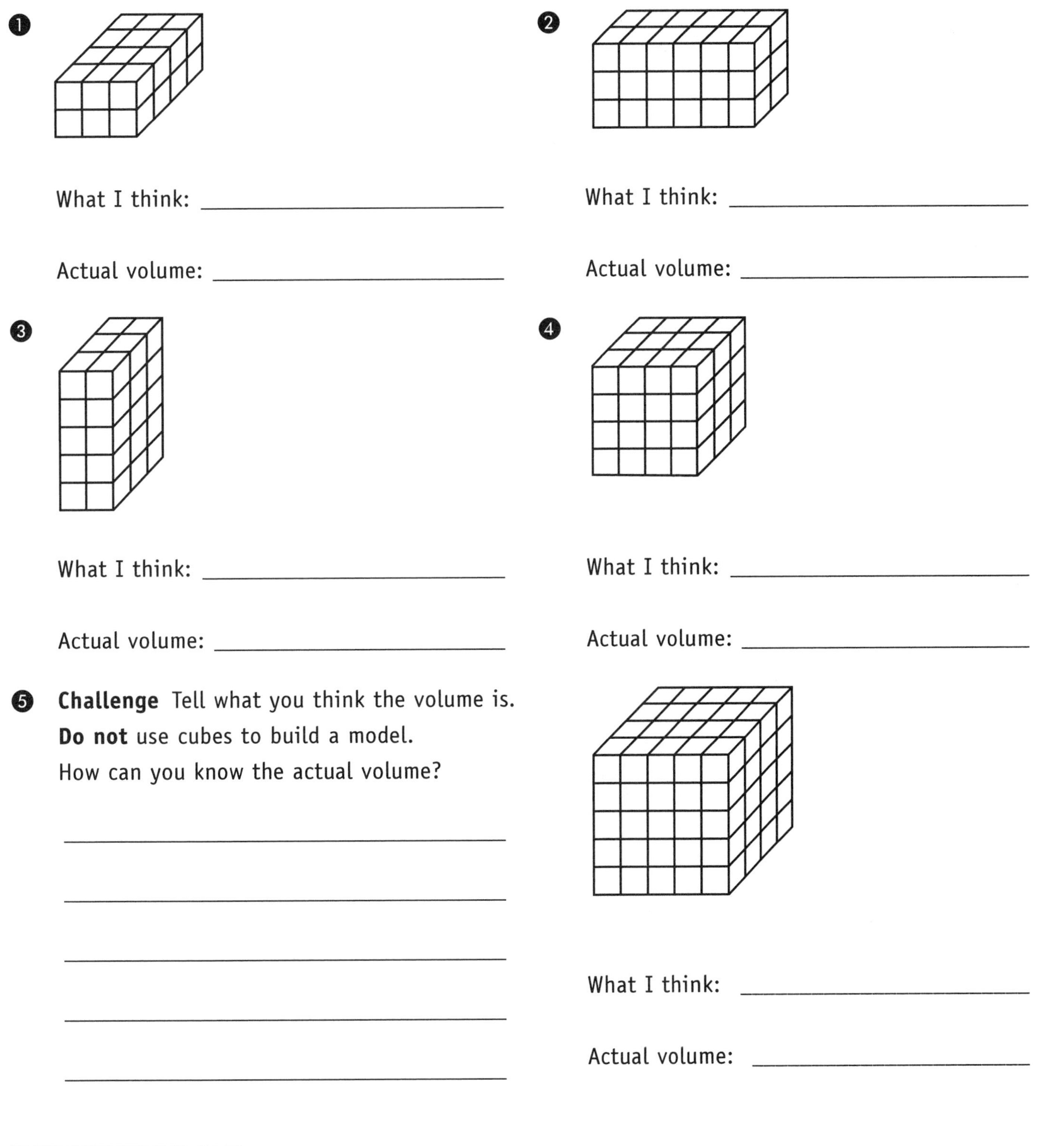

1. What I think: ______________________

   Actual volume: ______________________

2. What I think: ______________________

   Actual volume: ______________________

3. What I think: ______________________

   Actual volume: ______________________

4. What I think: ______________________

   Actual volume: ______________________

5. **Challenge** Tell what you think the volume is.
   Do not use cubes to build a model.
   How can you know the actual volume?

   ____
   ____
   ____
   ____
   ____

   What I think: ______________________

   Actual volume: ______________________

© Creative Publications Permission is given by the publisher to reproduce this page for classroom or home use only.

Estimating Metric Units of Length

Introduction

Objective → Students will estimate metric units of length.

Context → Students have discussed different units of measure in the metric system and have measured lengths to the nearest centimeter. They will go on to measure greater metric lengths with a ruler.

Estimating Metric Units of Length

Learn

Like the centimeter (cm), the **decimeter (dm)**, the **meter (m)**, and the **kilometer (km)** are metric units used to measure length and distance.

A decimeter is about the length of 4 quarters in a row.

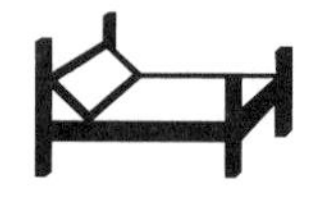

A meter is about the width of a twin-size bed.

A kilometer is about how far you could ride a bicycle in 8 minutes.

The chart below shows how these units relate to one another.

10 centimeters (cm)	=	1 decimeter (dm)
10 decimeters (dm)	=	1 meter (m)
100 centimeters (cm)	=	1 meter (m)
1,000 meters (m)	=	1 kilometer (km)

Tell whether you would use cm, dm, m, or km to measure the following:

1. your height

2. the distance from Kansas to Georgia

3. the length of a school bus

4. How did you decide which units to use to measure each of these?

NCTM Process Standards Analysis and Focus

The standards analysis examines how the process standards have been incorporated into the above lesson. By increasing the focus on three of the process standards, a more effective and meaningful lesson can be presented. The suggestions offered can help you to think about how this might be accomplished.

Representation Useful connections are made between units of measure and familiar items that represent those units. Equivalent measures are represented in a chart on the student pages.

Suggestion → **Personalize the metric lengths focused on in the lesson by having students identify familiar items as well as places on their body to represent those units. This will provide**

© Creative Publications

Try

What unit would you use to measure the following? Write the letter for the unit you choose.

5. the length of a paper clip	**a.** cm	**b.** dm	**c.** m	**d.** km
6. the width of your classroom	**a.** cm	**b.** dm	**c.** m	**d.** km
7. the distance from the earth to the moon	**a.** cm	**b.** dm	**c.** m	**d.** km
8. the length of a dollar bill	**a.** cm	**b.** dm	**c.** m	**d.** km

Practice

What unit would you use to measure the following?

9. the length of a soccer field
10. the length of a shoelace
11. the distance between two cities
12. the width of your thumb

Choose the best estimate.

13. the length of a table	**a.** 20 dm	**b.** 20 m	**c.** 20 km
14. the height of a building	**a.** 120 m	**b.** 120 km	**c.** 120 cm
15. the width of a doorway	**a.** 1 m	**b.** 1 cm	**c.** 1 dm
16. the distance a car travels in an hour	**a.** 70 dm	**b.** 70 m	**c.** 70 km

Estimate the measurement of the following objects. Use a ruler or tape measure to find the actual measurement.

	Estimate	Actual Measure
17. the length of your desk (dm)	________	________
18. the distance from your elbow to your wrist (cm)	________	________
19. the width of the chalkboard (m)	________	________

Mixed Applications

20. Kyla ran 4 km on Monday, 3 km on Wednesday, and 5 km on Friday. How many km did she run in all?

21. Charlene grew 6 cm last year and 5 cm this year. How much has she grown in the past two years?

students with a basis for comparison that has personal meaning.

Communication Answering questions is limited to selecting a response from a listing of possible answers.

Suggestion → **Increase opportunities for students to discuss how they select units by which to measure and the strategies they use to estimate. This will help them develop and increase their own strategies and procedures. By writing about their strategies, students make their estimation process explicit and clarify their reasoning.**

Reasoning and Proof In an introductory exercise, students are asked to select a unit with which to measure an item and tell how they decided which measure to use.

Suggestion → **Help students gain greater experience in determining units to use when measuring an object by having them estimate the object's length and then measuring it. Encourage students to explain how they select the units they choose and how they arrive at their estimates. This will help students focus on the relative sizes of metric units and help them refine their estimation skills.**

Connections In this lesson, connections are intertwined with representation. Units are connected with familiar items and equivalent measures that represent them.

Problem Solving Estimating measurements requires making comparisons but it does not involve problem solving.

© Creative Publications

The teaching plan that follows shows how the suggestions for increasing the focus on the process standards can implemented.

Revised Teaching Plan

Materials → Meter sticks; metric rulers; measuring tapes; various objects for measuring (blocks, books, furniture, etc.); construction paper strips 1 decimeter long

Preparation → Prior to the lesson, prepare a list of items to be used for estimating and measuring activities found on page 118.

BEGIN THE LESSON with a review of centimeters. Talk about the size of a centimeter and explain that for many people, the width of their pinkie finger is about a centimeter. Show students how to measure the width of their pinkie fingers, and have them check to see whether their pinkie or a different finger is close to a centimeter in width. Next, have students work with a partner and take turns estimating the length of a few small items such as pencils or books in centimeters and then using a centimeter ruler to check their estimates. Ask students to describe for their partners why they estimated as they did.

Introduce decimeters by explaining that a decimeter is 10 centimeters long. *How many pinkie fingers would that be?* Demonstrate how to place one pinkie next to another to estimate a defined span on the overhead. Have students verify by repeating the procedure using a centimeter ruler.

Distribute paper decimeter strips and instruct pairs of students to use them to identify the span of a decimeter on their hands. Suggest that they start at the heel of their hand and determine whether the length to one of their fingertips is close to a decimeter. Also, ask students to identify some classroom items such as a chalkboard eraser or book that can serve as a reference because they are about a decimeter long.

As students identify items in the room that they think might be about a decimeter long, encourage them to first use either pinkies or hand measurements to see if they are close. Then have them use rulers to verify how close their estimates are. As before, instruct students to work with partners and to discuss their strategies after each estimate.

© Creative Publications

INITIATE A CLASS DISCUSSION to allow students to describe their strategies and tell how they estimated the lengths of the objects they have measured so far. (Strategies might include forming a mental image of the length, or using a reference such as an object that is known to be about that measure and using that object as a basis of comparison.) Demonstrate thinking aloud to give students a model they can use when they estimate. Make sure to convey the idea that the estimation process involves a sequence of mental decisions in which the estimate is narrowed down as much as possible. *Let's see. A chalkboard eraser is about a decimeter long, and this book is longer than an eraser but not as long as two erasers. I'd say this book is about one-and-a-half decimeters long.*

What Might Happen . . . What to Do

Students may be dismayed that their estimates do not match the measurements they obtain. Explain that estimates are not expected to be exact and that the goal of this estimation is to find out about how long the object is. Point out that the measure might be slightly over or under and that's okay. What is important is to pick an appropriate unit of measure and come up with an estimate that is close to the actual measure.

NOW FOCUS ATTENTION on the meter. Instruct students to use meter sticks and to locate a section of their bodies representative of a meter. This might involve their arm span, or the height from the floor to their waistline, or any section that they are likely to remember.

Verify that students are making connections between the different units of measure they have used so far. Make sure students are aware that a meter is 100 centimeters or 10 decimeters. *If it's a meter from the floor to your waistline, how many decimeters is that? Why? How many centimeters would it be?*

© Creative Publications

Explain that a kilometer would be 1,000 metersticks laid end to end. *Would the classroom be a kilometer long? Why?* Have students lay meter sticks end to end to see how many meters are needed to measure the room. Ask students about how many rooms, end to end, would be a kilometer. Ask several students to estimate the length of the hallway, and send a small group to measure it with meter sticks. *Is the hallway kilometers long? How many times would you have to walk back and forth the length of the hallway to walk a kilometer?*

Distribute a prepared list of several objects and instruct students to determine the most appropriate unit with which to measure each item. Include such items as a banana, a desk, the length of the playground, the length/height of the chalkboard, the length/height of the classroom, and the distance from the school to the end of the next block. Tell students to think about the activities already completed as they make their choices. As students respond, ask them to describe the strategies they used to make their decisions. *Would you use a meter to measure the length of a book? Why?* (No. A book is much shorter than a meter.) *Would decimeters or meters be the better units to measure the height of the room? Explain.* (The height of a room is better measured in meters.)

Extend the activity by writing the names of additional objects of different lengths/heights on individual slips of paper. Have students take turns picking a slip, locating the item, identifying which unit they will use to measure it, and then estimating its length. Ask students to then write a sentence or two about how they decided which unit to use and why they estimated as they did. Finally, have students measure the object and record the measurement.

Conclude the lesson by reviewing the units of linear measure focused on in the lesson and their relationships to one another. Also, have students consider their estimation strategies. *Were your estimates more accurate with centimeters, decimeters, or meters? Was the measuring unit you chose always the best one to use, or might a different unit have been better? Explain.*

Student Pages

Students are now ready to complete exercises similar to those on the reduced student pages.

Assessment

As students participated in the different activities, there were ample opportunities to assess their ability to choose appropriate units, make careful estimates, and take actual measurements. As students discussed and wrote about why they chose a particular unit of measure and how they estimated the object's length, it was possible to determine how well they grasped the concept of estimating metric units of length.

NCTM Standards Summary

By identifying familiar objects and parts of their bodies that represented different metric units, students developed handy references to use when making estimates. The lesson offered various opportunities for students to communicate their thinking. This helped them clarify their strategies for choosing appropriate units of measurement and for estimating lengths. Students' reasoning was engaged as they developed strategies with which to obtain relatively accurate estimates of metric lengths.

© Creative Publications

Standard 5 **Data Analysis and Probability**

AT THE FOURTH GRADE LEVEL, data analysis and probability include a lot of work with different graphical representations of data, statistical representations of a set of data, and probability concepts. Our lessons are derived from these important topics. They include a lesson on representing data, a lesson that introduces range, median, and mode, a lesson that explores probability, and a lesson on making and reading a bar graph.

Three lessons model how the process standards can be used to teach content. A fourth lesson is a hypothetical textbook lesson that we have revised to be more standards based. These four lessons do not represent the entire curriculum, but rather provide glimpses of how, with a more concentrated effort to incorporate the process standards, better mathematics teaching and learning can be achieved.

One lesson we have chosen asks students to choose and construct an appropriate graph for a given set of data. Students are often asked to interpret graphs that are presented, or to construct a particular type of graph for the data. By basing the lesson on the process standards

© Creative Publications

of communication, reasoning and proof, and representation, students make three different graphs for the same data, and have to decide which of the three makes the most sense to accurately represent the data.

Another lesson we have chosen has students comparing sets of data using the statistical measures of range, median, and mode. By making the process standards of communication, reasoning and proof, and representation a focus of this lesson, students are asked to do more than just identify the statistical measures. They are asked to choose which of the measures is best suited for a particular situation.

A third lesson we have chosen explores the two kinds of probability: mathematical probability and probability based on data. Through the process standards of reasoning and proof, connections, and communication, students analyze a probability experiment, comparing what they think will happen with what does happen. Students discuss the results and make generalizations about the two kinds of probability.

The hypothetical textbook lesson we have chosen to revise is one in which students create and interpret information in a bar graph. In many introductory lessons with comparable objectives, students are not generally provided with much instruction—it is assumed that the skills can be accomplished. Through better incorporation of the process standards of connections, representation, and communication, students are taught more about making a bar graph as well as what kinds of information are best represented in a bar graph.

Standard 5 Lessons

Representing Data

Exploring Range, Median, and Mode

Exploring Two Kinds of Probability

Making and Reading Bar Graphs

© Creative Publications

Representing Data

Introduction

Objective → Students will be able to choose and construct an appropriate graphic representation for a given set of data.

Context → Students have had several experiences working with data as well as constructing and interpreting different types of graphs. They are ready to look critically at data sets and determine the best graphic representation for the data given.

NCTM Standards Focus

Often students are presented with graphs already constructed and asked to interpret them. Rarely do students discuss graphs as communication devices and decide which type of graph best communicates the type of information they need to present. In this lesson, students will look at information they are asked to communicate and try to represent it in three different ways. As they make the graphs, they will focus on the advantages and disadvantages of using each type of graph to display a given data set.

Communication Communication is at the heart of this lesson. Students will understand that they are not just making graphs. Rather they are communicating information to other people. Through small-group and whole-class discussion, they will analyze what kinds of graphs best communicate what kinds of data.

Reasoning Students use reasoning skills to determine the best type of graphic representation for a given data set. They explain their reasoning and justify their opinions as they present their graphs to the class.

Representation Students will look at how different representations of the same data, while factually accurate, leave different impressions and communicate ideas differently. Those students who believe that math is cut-and-dried, may get a different idea as they see that different representations of the same data are possible.

Teaching Plan

Materials → Student pages 126–127; graph paper; unlined paper; an example of a bar graph, a pictograph, and a line graph

BEGIN THE LESSON by showing students examples of a pictograph, a bar graph, and a line graph. Ask students to look carefully at the graphs and think about what information the graphs communicate and how. The following questions might help get a discussion started.

- *What is the purpose of the graph?*
- *What are the makers of the graph trying to tell you?*
- *Do you think they were successful? Why or why not?*
- *Did any one thing stand out about the graph?*

© Creative Publications

- *Do you think the graph's makers used the right type of graph? Why or why not?*
- *Would you have done anything different to make the graph convey its message better? What would you have done?*

Make sure you focus students' attention on the types of graphs and whether a particular type is suitable for communicating the graph's message. You may wish to mention the following as discussion points.

- A pictograph is often good for comparing data that is concrete and visual, such as hamburgers sold per day of the week.
- A bar graph is also good for comparing data. The height of the bars can show the scale of the difference among data points. Bar graphs are also good for displaying information that is not visual and concrete, such as the times of five different swimmers in a race.
- A line graph is good for showing trends, such as the high temperatures for a week.

Make sure students end the discussion with the following points in mind.

- People make graphs to convey information—in effect, they tell a story.
- Reading a graph requires more than just pulling out pieces of information; it is like reading a story.
- Before making a graph, a person needs to have a clear understanding of what he or she wants the graph to communicate.

CONTINUE THE LESSON by putting students in groups of three. Distribute graph paper and a copy of student page 126 to each student. Tell students that the task of each group is to display each set of data in three ways—in a pictograph, in a bar graph, and in a line graph. As students work on their graphs, encourage them to talk among themselves about the strengths and weaknesses of each type of graph as it relates to the information students are trying to convey. Also, have them consider why it is more difficult to graph some kinds of data using a particular type of graph.

Students may find it difficult to make the three graphs for each data set, but they should try several ideas so they can better understand why some graphs may be easier than others for use in some situations.

f.y.i.

Grouping students in threes is recommended for this lesson, since each group will have the task of constructing three different graphs. However, other groupings will work.

When the groups have finished making their graphs, gather the class together for a discussion about what they have discovered. *Which graph best conveys the information in each data set? Why? Would another type of graph also display the information effectively? Why?* While there are no hard-and-fast answers to these questions, students need to justify their opinions with solid explanations. Encourage students to make generalizations about the kinds of data sets that are best displayed by each type of graph. *What kinds of data are easy to show in a pictograph? What kinds are difficult to show in a pictograph?* Continue the same line of questioning for the bar graphs and the line graphs. Below, are some points you may want to mention if they do not come up in the discussion.

- The data about sunset times is best represented in a line graph, since the goal is to show change over time. A bar graph, with bars close together, could also be used. It, too, would show change over time. It is difficult to show the sunset data on a pictograph. Pictographs are better suited to data that can be visualized as objects and counted.
- The park information could be displayed in a pictograph or bar graph. A pictograph would be more interesting. The line graph probably does not add anything because there is no trend over time that is being looked at.
- The school store study may be best in a bar graph since the goal is to compare information. A pictograph would give a less exact picture of the data since there will need to be partial units. The line graph probably does not add anything because there is no trend over time that is being looked at.

f.y.i.

There are many things that people can do with graphs to enhance a point of view. While the focus of this lesson is on types of graphs, some students may notice that they can do things, such as adjusting scale, to better show a point of view. Depending on the time you have, you may want to discuss this.

Student Pages

Student page 126 provides the data for use in class. Student page 127 gives students a situation, then asks them to make the appropriate graph and explain why they believe the type of graph they chose is the best for displaying the information.

Assessment

While students worked in groups, you had opportunities to observe them reason and select what they felt to be the best graphic representation of the data. You were able to assess their communication and reasoning skills, as groups made presentations to the whole class.

NCTM Standards Summary

In this lesson, students participated in the process of thinking about how to convey information by deciding which type of graph would best communicate that information. They then constructed a graphic representation of the data.

Answers

Page 126
Answers will vary; suggested answers are in the lesson.

Page 127
Answers may vary.

Name

Representing Data

Make a graph to show the data.

1. Jose noticed that it was staying lighter each day. He found the following information telling how much later the sun was setting each Sunday during March. He wants to make a graph that will convince his classmates that the sun is setting later each day.

Time Period	Time
Week of March 1st	5:55 p.m.
Week of March 8th	6:04 p.m.
Week of March 15th	6:14 p.m.
Week of March 22nd	6:23 p.m.
Week of March 29th	6:30 p.m.

2. A park manager has noticed that on some days the park is very crowded. The manager would like to make a graph to show visitors when the park is likely to be most crowded. She hopes that some people will decide to return to the park when it is not busy.

Day	Number of Visitors
Sunday	250
Monday	30
Tuesday	55
Wednesday	60
Thursday	70
Friday	125
Saturday	200

3. The school store manager has a record of items that were sold last week. She wants to make a graph to show visually how popular each item was.

Item	Number Sold
Tablets	55
Pencils	75
Color Pencil Sets	15
Notebooks	40
Rulers	25

Name ______________________

Representing Data

Read the information and make a graph you feel is the best one to communicate the information. Tell why you think it is the best graph to show the information

1. You are recording the height of a plant you are growing.
   You want to show people how quickly the plant grows.
   You have measured it each week for six weeks.

Week	1	2	3	4	5	6
Height of Plant in inches	1	2	4	6	7	7

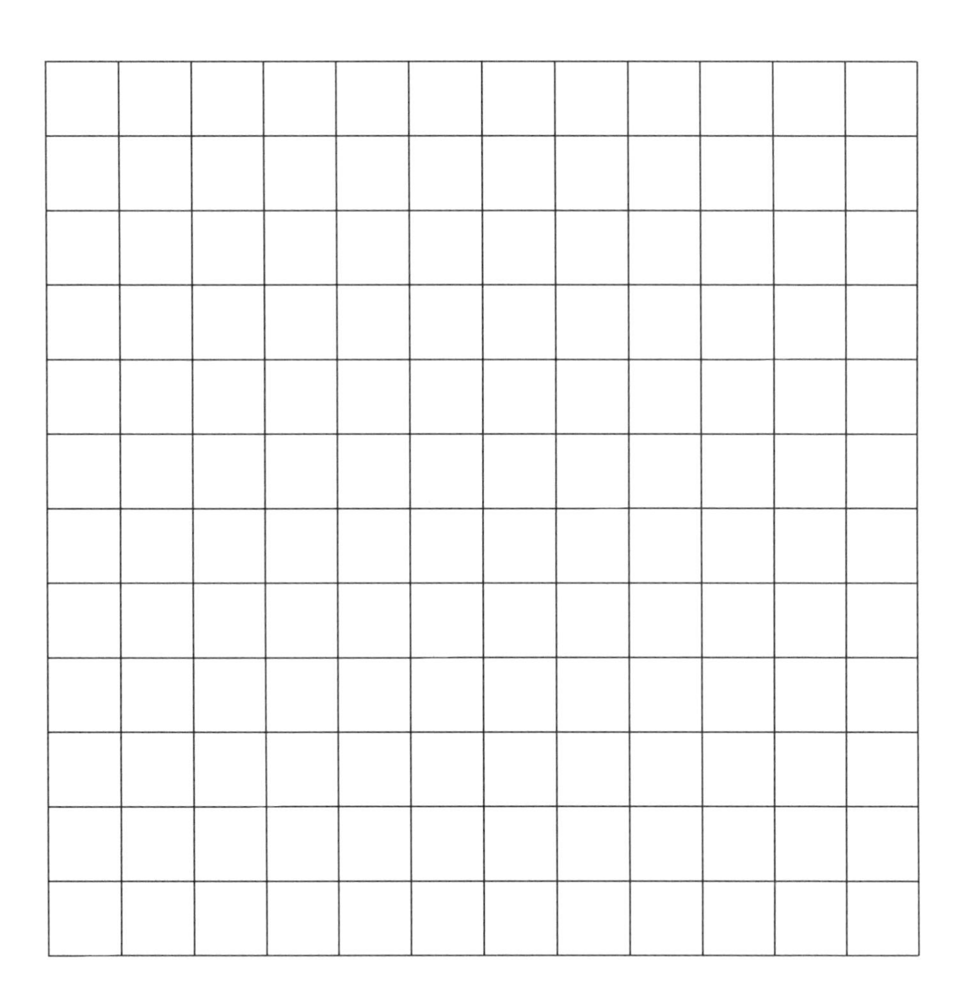

Exploring Range, Median, and Mode

Introduction

Objective → Students will be able to compare sets of data using range, median, and mode.

Context → Students have worked with various data sets and informally looked for ways to interpret the data. Understanding these measures will lay the foundation for future experiences with analyzing data and learning new measures (i.e., mean).

NCTM Standards Focus

Often students are presented with rules for finding these measures, then asked to find the measures for a series of data sets. In this standards-based lesson, students physically move around the classroom to model data and explore how to find these measures. They then apply this learning to real-world situations, using these measures to interpret given situations.

Problem Solving Students work with different sets of data and look for ways to best interpret the data. They respond to a couple of problem-solving situations by referring to the data's range, median, and mode.

Reasoning and Proof Students respond to situations where they must reason which data measure (range, median, mode) best tells the story behind the data.

Communication Students work together as a class and in small groups to explore the concepts of range, median, and mode. Initially they participate in an exercise where they physically move around the classroom to demonstrate these measures. This requires considerable communication on students' parts. Later, students communicate their understandings of these measures when working on problem-solving situations. They communicate their reasoning orally and in writing.

Representation Students construct a "human" data set and use it to explore range, median, and mode. This concrete representation of a data set allows students to internalize concepts rather than memorize rules and formulas.

Teaching Plan

Materials → Student pages 132–133

BEGIN THE LESSON by having each student write the number that corresponds to the day of his or her birthday (a number between 1 and 31) on a piece of scratch paper. Tell students that they have just created a data set and are going to explore some important data measures with their numbers. Let them know that this will be useful as they explore different sets of data later on in the lesson.

Find an area in the classroom or hall where there is room for students to move around. Instruct students to form a straight line, facing you, in order of their birthday numbers from the least number to the greatest. Designate where you want students to begin and end the line, then give them just a few minutes to place themselves in line. Students will need to talk with one another so that they can place themselves in the proper order.

Once students think they are in numerical order, have students count off as a check. If any students are out of order, have them move to their proper places in the line. When finished, students should be in one straight line, facing you, with their numbers in order from least to greatest.

f.y.i.

If there is not space available for students to line up, you can list the numbers on the board. Ask students to devise a method for listing the numbers in order.

EXPLAIN THAT WHAT THEY have just done is organize their data. Let them know that this is a critical first step that will now allow them to look at three different measures: *range*, *median*, and *mode*. To demonstrate range, have the student at one end of the line take a giant step forward. Do the same with the student at the other end of the line. Ask both students what their numbers are, then record these on the board. *What is the range of the numbers in this line?* Some students are likely to respond with an interval "from . . . to . . ." *What is the difference between the greatest number and least number? How can we determine this?* Allow students to respond with their methods, then record the range on the board. Tell students that in finding the difference between the greatest and least numbers, they found the range for the data set.

To continue the lesson, have the two students at either end return to their places in line. Tell students that the next measure they are going to explore is the *median*. Explain that the median is the middle number in a set of data when the data is in numerical order. To find the median, students need to find the middle student. With your students already in numerical order, they are ready to find this measure. Ask students how they might be able to locate the middle student. Use one of their suggestions.

f.y.i.

One way to locate the middle student is to have one student at each end of the line take a giant step forward. Continue this process, two students at a time, one from each end, until there are only one or two students remaining.

If there is one student in the middle, explain that this student represents the median, the middle number of the data set. If there are two students in the middle, ask students how they could determine the middle number.

Methods Students Might Use

- If the two numbers are the same, use that number.
- Count up from the lower number and back from the greater number until the middle number is reached.
- Add the two numbers and divide the sum by two.

Point out that the median does not have to be one of the data values. *How many numbers are below (or less than) the middle number? How many numbers are above (or greater than) the middle number?*

f.y.i.

Some students may benefit from a visual representation of finding the median when there are two "middle" numbers. You may want to use a number line to provide this visual representation and also to confirm that the computational method described really works.

FOR THE FINAL MEASURE, have students return to one straight line (again in the order of their birthday numbers). This time, tell them that you want them to make rows of same numbers. Students should continue to face you and the first person (in numerical order) with a given number should stay in place. Other students with matching numbers should then stand in a line behind the first person until all students are either standing alone or are in a line behind others. Check to make sure students are all properly placed. Once they are, have students turn around and face away from you. Explain that what they have just constructed is a human bar graph of their data.

Define the final measure, *mode*, as the number or value that appears most often in a set of data. *Would the data need to be in numerical order to determine this measure?* (No.) Have students look from where they are standing and see if they can find the mode of this set of data. *What number occurs most often? Which bar of the graph is the longest?*

The data for your class may not have an easily identifiable mode. If two or more dates are tied for the most occurrences, then each date is considered to be a mode of the data. A set of data may have more than one mode. If all of the dates occur only once, then there is no mode for the data.

Arrange students in groups of 3–4. Pass out a copy of student page 132 to each student. Point out that in both situations presented on this page, students are presented with a data set. Instruct students to find the different measures, then use these as a way of describing the data.

Once students have completed page 132, have each group present their responses and reasoning. Allow other groups to question the presenting groups. Some questions follow that you may want to include in the discussion.

- *Did the class do poorly, OK, or pretty well on the spelling test? Explain why you think so.*
- *Why not recite all 28 scores to the other teacher? Is there a better way to let her know how the class did?*
- *Which measure or measures best represent each set of data? Explain.*

- *Which measure(s) do not reflect the data well? Why?*
- *Which measure best supports your selection of a partner? Why?*

Allow for a lengthy discussion to take place revolving around the data sets and the different measures used to interpret the data. Try to get students to see that depending on the data and the questions asked, some measures give a better picture than others do. This is why students need to begin looking closely at data to begin to understand the various measures and how they can be used to tell a story about the data.

Student Pages

Student page 132 provides two situations where students are asked to interpret data. In each case, students are expected to refer to the range, median, and mode. Student page 133 provides students with eight practice problems where they are to find the range, median, and mode for given data sets.

Assessment

While students physically moved around the room to demonstrate how to find the different measures, you assessed their understanding of the process. Through questioning, you were able to identify those who understood what they were demonstrating and those who were unclear. You assessed the need for working through a second class example and made the decision whether or not this was necessary. While students worked in their groups, you observed their ability to transfer their learning to problem-solving situations. You assessed their ability to not only identify the different measures, but also to use these measures to describe the data. Finally, you were able to assess students' ability to work on their own to identify the range, median, and mode for eight different sets of data.

NCTM Standards Summary

In this lesson, students worked as a class to demonstrate how to find the range, median, and mode of a given set of data. This process involved a great deal of cooperation and communication on the part of the students. Students then engaged in two problem-solving situations where they identified and used these measures to interpret data. In each case, students presented their results and reasoning to the class.

f.y.i.

You may want to work through the first data set by having students physically represent the measures once again. This will reinforce the process for finding each measure. Students can then be assured that they're on common ground when responding to the first written question.

Answers

Page 132

1. Students should report that the class did well. Range = 8; median = 18, mode = 19.
2. Bowler A is the more consistent bowler. Range = 22; median = 121; mode = 126. Bowler B has the two highest scores. Range = 53; median = 103; mode = 124.

Page 133

1. Range = 12; median = 8; mode = 8.
2. Range = 19; median = 9; mode = 4.
3. Range = 29; median = 25; mode = 34.
4. Range = 22; median = 27; mode = 18, 27.
5. Range = 8; median = 43; mode = 43.
6. Range = 72; median = 44.5; mode = 45.
7. Range = 57; median = 37; mode = 16, 42, 49.
8. Range = 77; median = 45; mode = no mode.

Name ____________________

Exploring Range, Median, and Mode

A teacher showed her students' spelling test scores to another 4th grade teacher. There were 20 words on the test.

16, 18, 13, 19, 19, 20, 15, 14, 15, 12, 20, 20, 19, 18,
19, 17, 15, 19, 19, 20, 18, 17, 19, 16, 20, 18, 17, 19

1. How did the class do? Refer to the range, median, and mode in your answer.

____

____

____

____

____

____

Below are the last ten bowling scores of two of the school's best 4th grade bowlers.

Bowler A: 108, 112, 125, 126, 117, 126, 119, 130, 123, 114
Bowler B: 124, 94, 141, 104, 88, 124, 102, 135, 100, 95

2. What can you tell about the bowlers? Who would you pick as a partner? Why?

____

____

____

____

____

____

Name ____________________

Exploring Range, Median, and Mode

Find the range, median, and mode for each data set.

1. 13, 8, 5, 5, 14, 11, 8, 6, 15, 8, 3

   range = __________ median = __________ mode = __________

2. 9, 4, 21, 9, 4, 17, 9, 11, 4, 23, 6, 4

   range = __________ median = __________ mode = __________

3. 17, 34, 25, 22, 34, 41, 12, 34, 28, 22, 19

   range = __________ median = __________ mode = __________

4. 18, 38, 27, 34, 20, 16, 26, 27, 30, 18, 32

   range = __________ median = __________ mode = __________

5. 43, 45, 43, 41, 44, 45, 40, 48, 43, 44, 41, 43

   range = __________ median = __________ mode = __________

6. 83, 37, 45, 94, 22, 43, 27, 68, 76, 45, 39, 44

   range = __________ median = __________ mode = __________

7. 35, 16, 24, 49, 38, 16, 19, 53, 42, 49, 27, 71, 36, 42, 14, 48

   range = __________ median = __________ mode = __________

8. 59, 36, 22, 37, 41, 67, 31, 54, 93, 72, 43, 24, 38, 50, 99, 63, 47, 34

   range = __________ median = __________ mode = __________

Exploring Two Kinds of Probability

Introduction

Objective → Students will be able to describe the difference between mathematical probability and probability based on data.

Context → Students have worked informally with probability. They understand how to form simple fractions and what fractions mean. Students will continue to determine probabilities in situations with increasing numbers of outcomes.

NCTM Standards Focus

Students encounter probability situations in their everyday lives and basic probability concepts can be explained by connecting to these experiences. In this standards-based lesson, students engage in a hands-on probability experiment designed to generate a significant amount of data. This will enable students to compare mathematical and experimental probabilities and to recognize the relationship between the two.

Reasoning and Proof Students will analyze the situation of flipping a coin and explain how they determined mathematical probability. They will compare what they expect to happen with experimental results and generalize about the two kinds of probability.

Connections The connection between experimental and mathematical probability is a key focus of the lesson. Students will rely on prior knowledge about fractions to express chance as a measure. By connecting to real-life situations, students will reinforce their understanding of the fundamental concepts of probability explored in this lesson.

Communication Students will discuss how chance is involved in different situations. They will communicate their understandings of probability concepts both orally and in writing.

Teaching Plan

Materials → Student pages 138–139; pennies

INTRODUCE THE LESSON by discussing familiar situations in which people talk about the chance of something happening. Encourage students to give examples of situations that involve chance. These might include a weather reporter talking about the chance of rain, a sports team being given a certain chance of winning a game, familiar board or computer games, or television shows where a contestant spins a wheel.

Explain that probability is a measure of chance and that in this lesson they will be looking at different situations to determine the probability of something happening.

Ask students if they know what is meant by a "fair" coin. Make sure they understand that a fair coin is one with heads on one side and tails on the other and that, when flipped, is equally likely to land on either side. *If you flip a fair penny, how many different ways can it land? Explain.* (2; it can either land with heads up or with tails up.) *Do both have the same chance of happening?* (Yes.) Make clear that because getting heads on a coin flip is one of two possible things that can happen, we say the probability is 1 out of 2 (or $\frac{1}{2}$). *What is the probability of getting tails?* (Also $\frac{1}{2}$)

Explain that when we find a probability by thinking about what should happen, the probability is called *mathematical probability*. Sometimes we find a probability by using information from actual experience. The process of gathering this information is called an *experiment* and consequently, this second kind of probability is called *experimental probability*.

HAVE STUDENTS WORK in pairs to explore both kinds of probability by performing their own experiments. Distribute a copy of student page 138 and a penny to each pair of students. Direct their attention to the table for Round 1 on the worksheet and explain that they are to flip a penny 10 times and record the *outcome* each time by making a mark in either the heads or tails column. When they have completed all 10 flips, they are to enter the total for each column at the bottom.

Before beginning the experiment, have students predict the results they will get. *What do you think the total for heads will be for your 10 flips? Tails? Why?* (Students may say that for half of the outcomes heads should come up and for the other half tails should come up, so the results should be 5 heads and 5 tails.) Instruct students to write their predictions for both heads and tails under each column and then proceed with the experiment.

After students have completed Round 1, discuss their findings. Make sure all groups summarize their results. *How many heads did you get? How many tails? How did your results compare to your prediction? If the results were very different from your prediction, why do you think this is so?* (Many students will not have a response, but some may suggest that more tries are needed.)

Remind students of how the mathematical probability of $\frac{1}{2}$ for getting heads or tails was determined. Explain that the experimental probability is found by comparing the number of favorable outcomes with the total number of flips of the coin. The experimental probability for getting heads would be the number of times heads actually came up over the total number of flips (in this case, 10). Have students find the experimental probabilities for Round 1 and compare their results with the mathematical probabilities. *Does a mathematical probability of $\frac{1}{2}$ mean that something will always happen $\frac{1}{2}$ of the time?* (No.) *Can mathematical and experimental probabilities have different values?* (Yes.) *What does mathematical probability tell you?* (What should happen.) *What does experimental probability tell you?* (What actually happened.)

f.y.i.

Experimental Probability

$P(\text{event}) = \dfrac{\text{number of favorable outcomes}}{\text{total number of trials}}$

Ask students to offer predictions for outcomes for Round 2. Encourage students whose predictions and outcomes differed considerably in Round 1 to explain their thinking for predicting what might happen in Round 2.

What Students Might Say

- A student who had a 7 to 3 split might predict a 3 to 7 result for Round 2, reasoning that maybe the outcomes will even out.
- A student with a 9 to 1 split might predict another 9 to 1 split, thinking that perhaps his or her coin is not fair.
- A student with a 5 to 5 split might think he or she completed Round 1 correctly and will repeat the performance.

Have students complete Round 2 and discuss their results by answering questions similar to those for Round 1. Point out that while different groups may have gotten different individual results from Round 1, a similar overall variation between predicted and actual results occurred. Then let students move on to Round 3.

AFTER STUDENTS HAVE COMPLETED Round 3, have them explore how having a larger number of coin flips and outcomes affects the comparison between the two kinds of probability. Instruct students to find the total number of heads and the total number of tails for all three rounds. *If the probability was exactly $\frac{1}{2}$, how many heads should you have?* (15) *How many tails?* (15) *Are the total results closer to the mathematical probability than those for each separate round?* You may also wish to combine results for the whole class to produce numbers that are even closer to $\frac{1}{2}$.

Summarize the important ideas of the exploration. Emphasize that as students just saw, what should happen (mathematically) usually does not occur. Explain that as the number of times an experiment is repeated gets very large, for example one thousand or even one million times, the predicted results and the actual results should get closer. Use the class totals to justify this statement. You might want to encourage students to give intuitive explanations of why this is so. (They may suggest that lots of tries allows the results to "even out" or "balance out.")

If time allows, close the lesson by posing a situation for students to consider. *You flip a penny. It lands heads. The next time you flip the coin, is the probability of getting heads less than, equal to, or greater than* $\frac{1}{2}$*? Explain your reasoning.*

Students may think the chance of getting heads has been "used up," so the probability for getting heads is less. Or, they may think the first flip of heads shows you are more likely to get heads again. Explain that the penny doesn't "remember" the last flip, and the probability of $\frac{1}{2}$ does not change.

Student Pages

Student page 138 provides recording charts for the penny-flipping experiment. Page 139 presents students with mathematical and experimental probability situations to be analyzed and explained.

Assessment

While students worked on their penny-flipping experiments, it was possible to assess their understanding of outcomes and probability and their ability to make predictions. You were able to observe their ability to apply this learning as they analyzed their experimental data and compared the predicted and actual results.

NCTM Standards Summary

In this lesson, students flipped pennies to explore the concepts of mathematical and experimental probability. Reasoning was employed as students used their understanding of these concepts to analyze and identify the type of probability being used in different situations. The activities in the lesson helped students to make the connection between mathematical and experimental probability and express this relationship in their own words. Students relied on prior knowledge about fractions to write and compare probabilities and linked the concept of chance to everyday situations. Throughout the lesson, students clarified their thinking about probability as they used written and oral communication.

Answers

Page 138
Answers will vary.

Page 139

1. 4 outcomes; red, blue, green, yellow
2. Each outcome has the same chances because the sections for each color are equal.
3. $\frac{1}{4}$; mathematical probability
4. $\frac{1}{4}$
5. 0; There are no purple spaces on the spinner.
6. 100; $\frac{1}{4}$ of $400 = 100$
7. 20 times
8. 10 times
9. $\frac{10}{20} = \frac{1}{2}$; experimental probability
10. No; The mathematical probability is $\frac{1}{4}$ and the experimental probability is $\frac{10}{20}$ or $\frac{1}{2}$. When the number of tries is small, what should happen and what actually happens is often different.
11. Answers may vary. There should be more red sections than any other color. One possible solution would be 3 red, 1 yellow, 1 blue, 1 green.

Name

Exploring Two Kinds of Probability

Flip a penny and place a mark to indicate whether it came up heads or tails. Repeat 10 times for each round.

Round 1

Heads	Tails

Round 2

Heads	Tails

Round 3

Heads	Tails

Totals of Rounds 1–3

Heads	Tails

Name

Exploring Two Kinds of Probability

Use the spinner shown at the right to answer the questions.

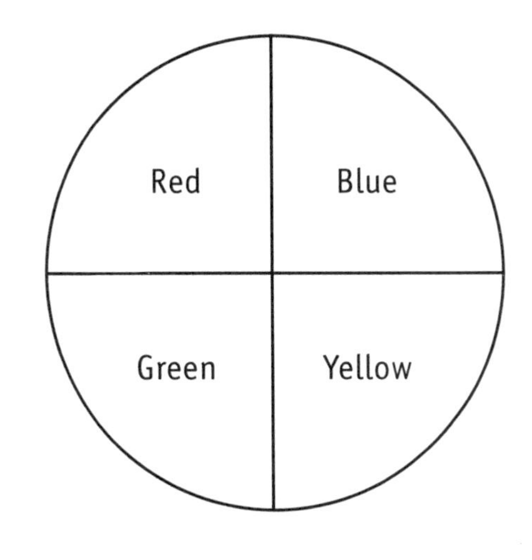

1. If you spin once, how many different outcomes are possible? What are they?
2. Does each outcome have the same chance? Explain why or why not.
3. If you spin once, what is the probability of spinning blue? What kind of probability is this?
4. If you spin once, what is the probability of spinning red?
5. If you spin once, what is the probability of spinning purple? Explain.
6. If you spin 400 times, about how many times would you expect to get green? Explain.

The table shows the results of Kevin's spins.

red	3
blue	10
green	5
yellow	2

7. How many times did Kevin spin?
8. How many times did Kevin spin blue?
9. Based on the results in the table, what is the probability of spinning blue? What kind of probability is this?
10. Compare your answers for questions 2 and 9. Are the answers the same? Explain why.
11. Label this spinner with color names to create a spinner for which the chances of getting red are greater than the chances for each of the other colors.

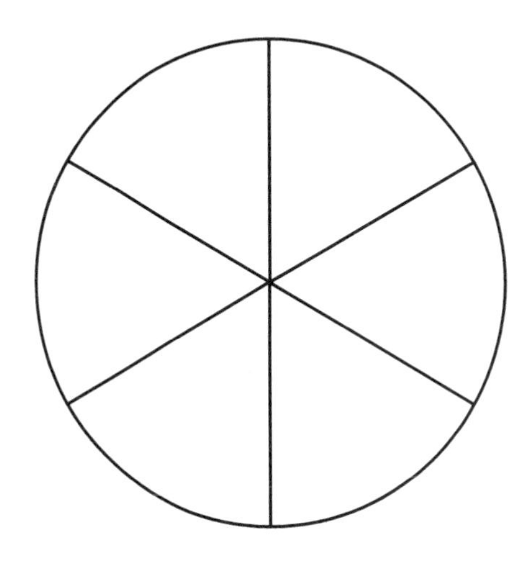

Making and Reading Bar Graphs

Introduction

Objective → Students will make and read bar graphs.

Context → This lesson comes at the beginning of a chapter in which students read and make graphs. After this lesson, students will work with pictographs and line graphs.

Making and Reading Bar Graphs

Learn

The graph shows the results of 50 tosses of a number cube.
Work with a partner. Copy the graph. Toss the cube 50 more times.
Record your results. Add your results to the graph. Finish the graph.

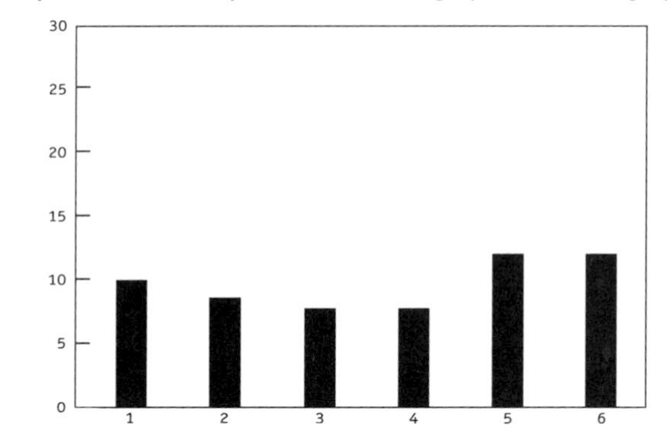

Answer these.

1. What do the bars tell you?
2. What new numbers did you write on the scale?
3. What would you call this graph?

How to Make a Graph

1. Make your title.
2. Make your scale.
3. Label the sides.
4. Make your bars.

Try

Take two different colored cubes. Put some of each in a bag.
Draw a cube. Record its color. Put the cube back.
Do this 40 times. Make a graph of the results.

NCTM Process Standards Analysis and Focus

The standards analysis examines how the process standards have been incorporated into the above lesson. By increasing the focus on three of the process standards, a more effective and meaningful lesson can be presented. The suggestions offered can help you to think about how this might be accomplished.

Connections The notes accompanying the lesson suggest tallying favorite foods and having students create a bar graph as an assessment.

Suggestion → **Using data about the students to create a graph is effective because it connects the students to the exercises and motivates learning. Rather than using this activity at the end of the lesson, consider using it to develop the lesson.**

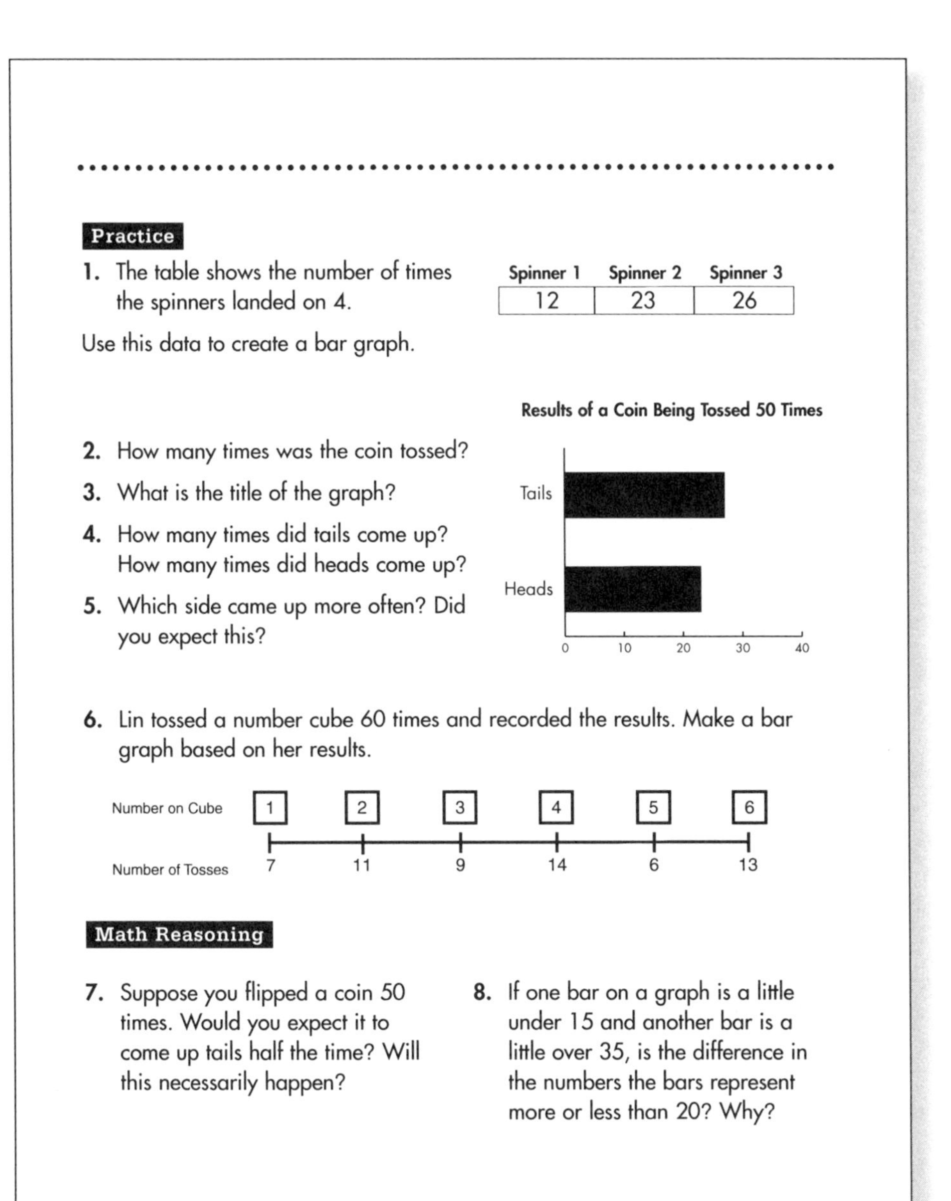

Practice

1. The table shows the number of times the spinners landed on 4.

Spinner 1	Spinner 2	Spinner 3
12	23	26

Use this data to create a bar graph.

2. How many times was the coin tossed?
3. What is the title of the graph?
4. How many times did tails come up? How many times did heads come up?
5. Which side came up more often? Did you expect this?

6. Lin tossed a number cube 60 times and recorded the results. Make a bar graph based on her results.

Number on Cube	1	2	3	4	5	6
Number of Tosses	7	11	9	14	6	13

Math Reasoning

7. Suppose you flipped a coin 50 times. Would you expect it to come up tails half the time? Will this necessarily happen?
8. If one bar on a graph is a little under 15 and another bar is a little over 35, is the difference in the numbers the bars represent more or less than 20? Why?

Representation The lesson does not clearly teach what the parts of a bar graph represent and how to interpret the bars themselves.

Suggestion → **Use the process of conducting a survey, organizing the data, and creating a bar graph to support student learning about how data can be represented by a bar graph. This process will help students develop a richer understanding of this form of representation. It will also help them with interpreting graphical representations of data.**

Communication In the directions for creating bar graphs, little attention is devoted to discussing how information in the graph is organized. Most of the exercises in the lesson can be answered with minimal discussion.

Suggestion → **Discuss the purpose of graphs in general and the advantages offered by bar graphs in particular. Increase discussion on how to interpret the data presented. Include discussion on what information should be included when creating a graph and how to best represent that information.**

Problem Solving While reasoning is required to interpret information, problem solving is not part of this lesson.

Reasoning and Proof The lesson offers a few questions that require students to interpret information, however, students are not asked to explain their thinking.

The teaching plan that follows shows how the suggestions for increasing the focus on the process standards can implemented.

Revised Teaching Plan

f.y.i.

If you do not have access to graphs to display, create simple graphs on large sheets of paper. They need not be fancy, but each should include a title and appropriate labeling information.

Materials → A collection of graphs for display; graph paper; ruler or straight edge; graph paper on transparency; overhead projector

Preparation → Prior to the lesson, gather a few types of graphs such as pictographs, circle, line, and bar graphs to display during the lesson. Make sure graphs are large enough to be seen by all students. Also make a transparency of the graphs in Figure A for demonstration.

BEGIN THE LESSON by telling students that they will be working with different types of graphs over the next several days. *What can you tell me about graphs?* Students have had previous experience with graphs, and their responses to this question will give you a sense of what they know about them. Listen for statements indicating that graphs are ways of representing information, that they are picture like, and that there are different kinds of graphs. Students may even be able to name different types of graphs. On the board, start a list of pertinent comments with the heading **Ideas on Graphs.** At the end of the lesson, you and your students will return to this list to refine and summarize information.

Display the prepared graphs. Discuss the features common to all graphs that allow us to interpret the information they contain. *What are some things that all of these graphs have in common?* (Title, labels that identify information, numbers) *Why are those things important to have on a graph?* For contrast, show the unlabeled and untitled graphs in Figure A. *What would happen if this identifying information were left out of the graph?* (We wouldn't know what the graph was about or what was being represented.) As students respond to questions, have the class decide about adding to the **Ideas on Graphs** list. Help students, as necessary, to rephrase and summarize the ideas before adding them to the list.

FOCUS STUDENTS' ATTENTION on bar graphs. *Which of these graphs is a bar graph? How do you know?* Tell students that they will be making a bar graph and that you will be asking them for some information to put into graph form.

Conduct a simple survey to gather data to put into graph form. Possible survey topics include the number of letters in first names of students, favorite animals for a pet, shoe size, favorite color, or favorite flavor of ice cream (limited to 3 or 4 choices). As you survey each student, record the data on the board. List the category and use tally marks for the number of students in the category. Have students help total the tally marks for each category and record the totals. (Leave this tally table on display so that students can refer to it later in this lesson.)

Guide students to consider how to represent the information just collected in a bar graph. *What title shall we give it? What will the bars in the graph represent? How will we know how long the bars should be? Should the bars be vertical (up and down) or horizontal (left to right)? When we complete this graph, what will it show? In what ways will it look different from the tally table we just created?* These questions may serve as a lead-in to a discussion about the appropriate scale to use for a graph, which can be a determining factor in the orientation of the graph.

Distribute graph paper. If the orientation of the graph has not been discussed yet, raise the topic with the class. Depending on how comfortable students are with graphing, you can either assign an orientation or allow students to choose their own. The idea that bar graphs that present the same data can look different will extend the learning about the representation of data.

MODEL HOW TO DRAW the axis lines, pointing out that students need to allow room for labeling each axis line. Move around the room to monitor students as they draw axis lines on their graph paper.

Next, label each axis. Begin with the axis that will represent the categories. Discuss how many bars need to be drawn and what each bar will represent. Point out that the bars should be the same width and distance from each other so that the graph is easy to read. Check that the bars will fit along the axis, and demonstrate how to mark points on the axis for each bar. Add labels. (Consider modeling a "mistake" such as drawing the axis line too short and then extending it once the categories are laid out. *We have five categories in our data, so we'll need room for five bars. But my graph isn't large enough to fit them all. What should I do?* Ask students to label this

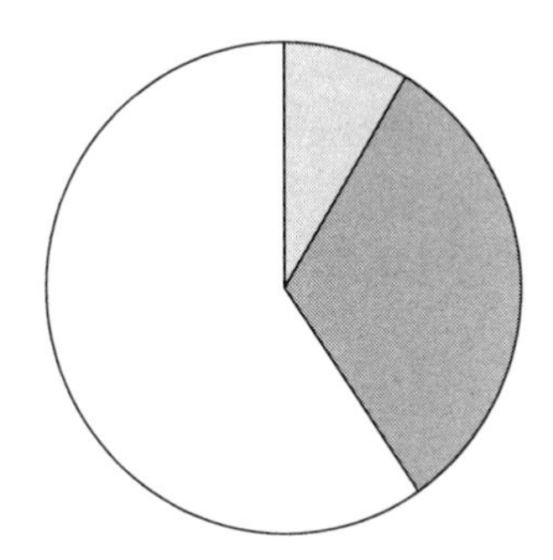

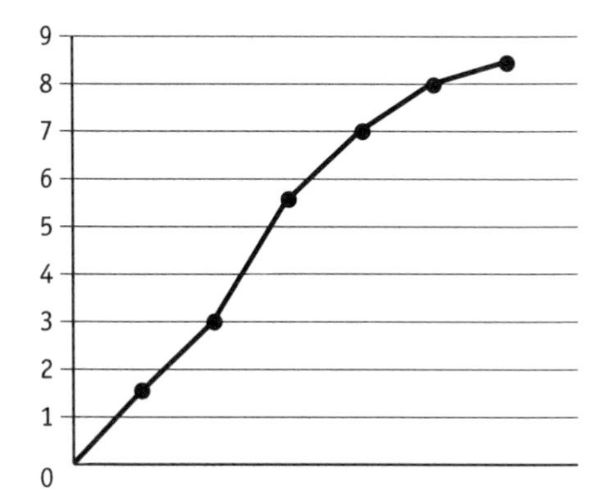

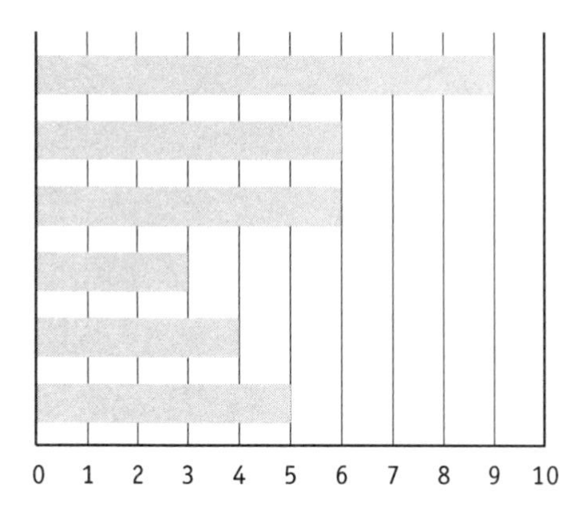

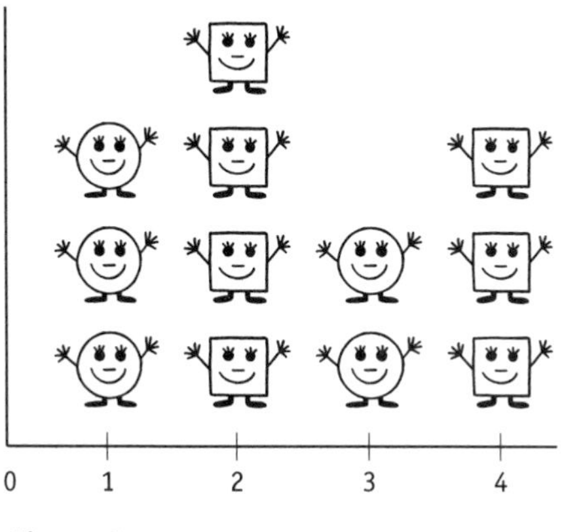

Figure A

axis on their graphs and mark out the base of each bar. Continue to monitor students, and provide help as needed.

Next, focus on the axis representing quantity. Tell students that where the bars begin along the category axis represents zero. Decide on the intervals that will be used on the quantity axis. If space will not be a problem, you might use intervals of 1 or 2; however, if the data spans a wide range, intervals of 5 or 10 might be appropriate. Explain that the numbers indicating intervals should always be equal increments. Emphasize the importance of equal spacing as the intervals are labeled. Then model how to mark intervals on the graph paper. *The largest bar will represent chocolate because there were 12 students who liked chocolate ice cream best. Will there be room to allow one square for each student?* Count out 12 squares to represent the bar for chocolate. Model labeling the quantity axis, and ask students to do the same. Stress the importance of doing this carefully, and monitor students as they work.

SHOW STUDENTS HOW TO CREATE a bar for one of the categories. If the data falls between intervals on the quantity axis, discuss how to judge at which point to place the top of the bar. Have students draw the remaining bars as you monitor their progress.

When the graphs are completed, ask interpretive questions about the information in the graph. You might use thumbs-up, thumbs-down votes to check individual student's agreement with each answer. This serves as a useful quick assessment at this point in the lesson. *Which flavor of ice cream was most popular? How many more students chose chocolate than vanilla? Which flavor was least popular? If we ranked the flavors in order of popularity, what would that order be?*

Direct students' attention to the tally table resulting from the survey. Point out that the information here and in the graphs is the same. *Why do we make graphs of information? What's the difference between these two representations of our survey data?* Students should agree that the picture-like format of the graph makes it more appealing to look at and helps to read information quickly. Point out that because of this fact, bar graphs make it easy to compare information. As the study of graphs progresses through the unit, you will want to help students understand why certain graphs are better for certain situations.

CLOSE THE LESSON by returning to the **Ideas on Graphs** list and refining the information. Encourage students to contribute information to add to the list. Include information that points out that bar graphs are useful for comparing information. *Is there anything else we can add about graphs in general or bar graphs in particular? Is there anything we should change or eliminate?* You might choose to copy this list onto chart paper, and post it for the remainder of the unit on graphs.

Student Pages

Students are now ready to complete exercises similar to those on the reduced student pages.

Assessment

The lesson provided opportunities to assess students' progress as they created bar graphs and discussed their form and function. As students answered questions and gave thumbs-up, thumbs-down votes during the discussion about the finished graph, there were opportunities to tell how well they understood bar graphs and could interpret the information presented.

NCTM Standards Summary

By participating in a survey, compiling and organizing data about themselves, and creating a bar graph based on the data they collected, students were able to make strong connections to the real-world applications of graphs. Students created bar graphs that represented specific data, and they interpreted information represented in bar graph form. Throughout the lesson, students had ample opportunities to communicate and summarize their ideas about the form and function of bar graphs.

Create Your Own Lesson

THIS LAST CHAPTER IS DESIGNED TO HELP you develop your own lessons in which you can comfortably incorporate the NCTM standards with your teaching style. We start with a list of questions to help you focus on factors to consider as you begin to organize a standards-based lesson. Then, we model the process used to create a lesson, as you are walked through the thoughts and decisions one person used in developing a lesson.

The questions listed here are meant as a guide, a starting point; they are offered to get you thinking about how to develop your lesson, what material to cover, what steps to follow, what questions to ask. Hopefully, these questions will trigger additional ideas that you will add as you go along.

Write down the ideas that come to you as you read each question. There may be questions for which you don't have an immediate response, but don't worry; as you begin working on your lesson, ideas will come. Start by selecting the general content area. Think about the concept you want to develop. Then, narrow in on an objective for the lesson. Be specific and be realistic. What does meeting that objective mean? Is there a skill that students should be able to perform after completing the lesson? Are there questions they should be able to answer? How will you determine that the objective has been met?

Next, think about the process standards: Problem Solving, Reasoning and Proof, Communication, Connections, and Representation. What approach will be effective in helping students understand the concept? Try to envision how the lesson will flow, how it should begin, what activities and questions will be included, and how you will assess learning. Understand that there can be several ways to successfully teach any lesson. As you begin to design your lesson, new ideas will come and you will be able to refine your thinking.

Focusing Questions

1. What content standard is to be addressed? What concept within that standard is to be developed?

2. What information do the standards offer about this content?

3. What do students know about this content? What don't they know?

4. What is the specific objective of the lesson? What should students be able to do at the end of the lesson?

recognize	**identify**	**define**
review	**compute**	**classify**
compare	**create**	**other**

5. What kinds of questions should students be able to answer when they complete this lesson? What skill(s) should they be able to demonstrate?

6. What resources are available to develop this concept?

references	**textual material**
manipulatives	**supplementary material**
colleagues	**student knowledge**

7. What can realistically be accomplished in the time allowed?

8. Which activities and process standards can best help develop the key ideas?
   - using drawings, charts, diagrams (Representation)
   - focusing on symbols (Representation)
   - conducting small-group/large-group discussion (Communication)
   - having students gather and analyze data (Problem Solving)
   - thinking through relationships and explaining them (Reasoning and Proof and Communication)
   - finding ways to prove thinking and verify solutions (Reasoning and Proof)
   - extending/building on former knowledge (Connections)
   - integrating the concept with another discipline (Connections)
   - relating math to its use in the real world (Connections)

9. What questions will focus students' thinking on the concept and help guide learning?

Developing the Lesson

I WANT TO DEVELOP A LESSON that involves estimating sums and differences, a topic that is part of the number and operations standard. Most lessons I have seen that address these skills, incorporate teaching/learning strategies and techniques such as front-end estimation and rounding. We have practiced those estimating techniques with multi-digit addition and subtraction. As I consider the standards, and their emphasis on problem solving, thinking, and the use of math in the world outside of the classroom, I think a lesson that focuses on when it is appropriate to estimate would really be beneficial to my students. Examining situations and deciding when to estimate should strengthen number sense and help broaden thinking about different approaches that can be used in solving problems.

My concern, as I think more about how to develop this lesson, is whether the lesson should include estimation strategies or just focus on having students decide when an estimate is an appropriate answer. Do I want students to estimate, or do I want them to determine whether or not an estimate is sufficient to solve the problem? I think that part of the lesson will need to deal with different types of estimation skills, so students can see that some strategies may work better in some situations than others.

When to estimate and when not to estimate has been discussed in some earlier lessons, but very little of the estimating has been in contextual situations. I'm not sure that students are aware of how often they estimate in their daily lives. It is certain they will use estimation in a number of situations as they get older. I recently read that research has shown that most of the mathematics we do in our daily lives—from 75% to 90%—is done with estimation. I feel comfortable that understanding when to estimate is an important skill for students to learn. However, this is a lesson I'll need to develop myself because it is not addressed in the textbook I use.

My objective will be to have students determine when problems can be answered with an estimate and when they require an exact answer. The process standard that immediately springs to mind is problem solving: posing real-life problem situations that will activate interest and make this lesson meaningful to my students. If I am going to ask students to solve problems and determine whether or not to use estimation, then it seems to me reasoning and proof will also be important. Students should be able to explain their procedures and justify their decisions.

As I see this lesson taking shape, with students being presented with problems, determining solution methods, and then justifying their thinking, I can see that communication will play a major role. I think a lot of students believe they always have to obtain an exact answer. So, as I challenge their beliefs, and they justify their solutions and clarify their understanding of this new concept, there will need to be a great deal of communication.

I've found ways that three of the process standards—problem solving, reasoning and proof, and communication—can help me develop this lesson. There are two other process standards, representation and connections, that can assist me, also. I think students will be most interested and become involved in the lesson if I use estimation problems that connect to their lives. Representation should flow naturally, as students show how they solved the problems and found ways to represent their thinking.

Now that I have a general plan, I need to focus on the specifics. I will present some problems and have students write out their answers. Then, we'll talk about their solutions. I'll ask students to tell whether they needed an exact answer to solve the problem or if an estimated answer was sufficient. In doing this, we will naturally look at different estimation strategies and decide how they relate to the problems. My hope is that this will cause students to look at estimation situations in a new light, and help them begin to develop a sense about when estimation is the best approach for a solution and when an exact answer is needed. I am not sure what else I will need to do, but I am going to start putting together the particulars and work from there.

The question I'll now ask myself is, *What estimation situation(s) can the students relate to that will get them involved in the lesson?* To answer this, I'll think about everyday situations in which I use estimation, and then I'll try to determine if these situations are ones my students might encounter. One thought that comes to mind is wanting to buy an item and determining whether I can make the purchase when I have limited funds. Buying food at a restaurant is a situation that I think many students may have experienced, and it is certainly one they are likely to encounter in the future.

THE ESTIMATION PROBLEMS I SELECT to begin this lesson are important; I want them to be real and to require students to think about the situation. One important difference I've noticed between most math problems presented in textbooks and the mathematical situations we face in our daily lives, is that problems in schoolbooks usually ask for a numerical answer: *How much was it? How much was left?* Real-life math problems often ask for decisions in which numerical information plays a part, but the solutions don't necessarily call for a numerical answer, such as: *Should you buy or lease a car?* I think presenting some problems in this decision-based format will encourage students to use estimation and will make the problems more relevant.

I'll create a price list for items that can be purchased at a restaurant and then prepare two estimation problems based on buying items from that list. Making a price list will make it easier for me to develop more estimation situations later in the lesson. The list will give me data to use during the lesson, too, so I can make up a problem on the spot or change a problem to one where estimation is not the best strategy. Also, I think I might want students to develop their own questions later. The price list will give me the flexibility to encourage communication and reasoning more easily as the lesson develops.

Price List

Item	Price
Hamburger	$1.09
Cheeseburger	$1.27
Double Hamburger	$1.99
Double Cheeseburger	$2.19
Special Sauce Burger	$2.48
Chicken Sandwich	$2.76
Chicken Strips	$3.38
Small French Fries	$0.77
Large French Fries	$1.19
Small Drink	$0.89
Large Drink	$1.07

Tax is included in the price of each item.

Problem 1

You are at the restaurant and have a $5 bill. Do you have enough money to buy a double cheeseburger, a special sauce burger, a large order of french fries, and a large drink?

Problem 2

You are at the same restaurant and have $4. Do you have enough money to buy a large drink, a small order of french fries, and two hamburgers?

I'll have students work in pairs to solve the problems. I'll instruct students to determine whether or not they should estimate in order to answer the question. They should agree on their decision. Then, they should solve the problem any way they choose. Pairs should be prepared to explain the method(s) they used to the rest of the class. The discussions after the problems are solved are very important because they provide opportunities to explain reasoning and to clarify ideas.

Discussing Problem 1

I'll prepare questions I can use to facilitate the discussion of the problem. *What is the first thing you did in trying to determine how to solve this problem?* I'll ask this question because I want students to step back and think about a problem before they rush into it and start calculating. In this instance, scanning the information and getting a general idea of the answer before they start to solve the problem, will help them see that estimating the solution is as far as students need to go in answering the question.

I'll ask each pair of students offering a solution, to convince the class that their answer is correct. Then, I'll survey the class to see if students are convinced, encouraging them to explain specifically why they are or are not. This type of questioning strategy requires students to use critical thinking, and their answers can help me assess whether they are getting the point.

As they present solutions and reasoning, I will invite the students in the class to challenge one another. If they let something go by, then I will confront it. Rather than pointing out errors, my goal will be to pose any questions that help students see flaws in their thinking. For example, if a student were to say that front-end estimation could always be used to solve a problem of the type that was just done, I would respond, *What if you had $7 instead of $5? Would you use front-end estimation to solve the problem then?* I would ask the student to convince us of his or her answer.

What type of estimation strategy could you use? With this question, I want students to be aware that different methods are possible, and that the types of estimation strategies spring out of the context of the problem. Students don't have to follow a particular method; in fact, they might often combine strategies. The answers to this question will give me information about the methods they have used. One possibility might be that students see that a double cheeseburger and a special sauce burger together cost close to $5. The special sauce burger is about $2.50 and the double cheeseburger costs a little more than $2. That leaves less that $1.

Would you advise someone to use front-end estimation in this situation or not? I would ask this question because I want to see if students understand that front-end estimation will always give an estimate that is less than the exact answer. If that estimate is higher than what you can accept, then you know that you cannot buy the items.

If you had $7, would using front-end estimation make you confident that you had enough money? Here students will see the other side of the situation. Front-end estimation would result in an answer that is less than the amount of money available, but not by much. Students then would need to either use another technique to refine their estimate or, in this case, find an exact answer.

Discussing Problem 2

With the second problem, I want students to examine at a similar situation, but one that has a different outcome. I think that most students will have to calculate to find that the cost of the meal is $4.02. I would pose the same initial question asked for the previous problem, *What is the first thing you did in trying to determine how to solve this problem?* Even students who solve the problem without writing it down on paper, should note that they found an exact answer rather than an estimate.

I would want my students to compare the two problems. *How are the two problems similar and how they are different?* The ensuing conversation should focus on some general ideas that can be used to determine whether estimation is sufficient to solve a problem or whether an exact answer is required.

Some students may think, *Why not always get an exact answer rather than estimate since you know that sometimes an estimate won't work?* I want students to realize that when they understand mathematics, they are the masters of a great tool. Thinking about a calculation rather than actually doing it can save them a great deal of time and energy. While the difference in the amount of time taken between getting an exact answer and estimating is not great in these problems, students will find that applying these techniques in more complex situations can save them a lot of time.

Following these two introductory estimation problems, I'll present additional situations based on the same price list. For each, I'll ask students to tell whether they should estimate or find an exact answer. Students have just begun to think about this topic, and I want them to wrestle with it some more. I also want them to create two math problems of their own, one that can be solved with estimation and one that needs an exact answer.

Additional Problems

You ordered a double hamburger, a cheeseburger, a small order of french fries, and a small soda. Your friend ordered a double cheeseburger, a cheeseburger, a large order of french fries, and a large soda. Whose bill was greater?

It is interesting to note when discussing this problem, that a different estimation technique can be used. Students do not actually have to find even an estimated total. By comparing the costs of similar items, they will find that the friend has ordered something more expensive in each case, and so had the greater bill.

How much change will you get back from a $20 bill if you order two double hamburgers, two chicken sandwiches, four large orders of french fries, and four large drinks? For this problem, students will need to find an exact answer. They will need to calculate either on paper or in their heads.

You are buying a chicken sandwich, a small order of french fries, and a small drink. You have $6. Can you also get a cheeseburger? This question is interesting because some students may think that the costs are so close, they cannot estimate. On the other hand, some students may see that it is possible to answer *yes* without calculating, since the small fries and small drink are less than a dollar each.

Reviewing the Plan

Before teaching this lesson, I need to review it to make sure it meets my goals and uses the standards effectively. I really feel a problem-solving approach, using a connection to real-life situations students might face, will inspire them to think about the focus of the lesson. Each problem allows students to consider whether to use estimation or an exact calculation to find the answer. Having students work in pairs encourages the communication of ideas. Having students reason through strategies and explain procedures, further extends communication while helping them clarify their thinking. The questioning techniques also make communication and reasoning and proof a major part of the lesson.